VISTA

AMERICAN SIGN LANGUAGE SERIES

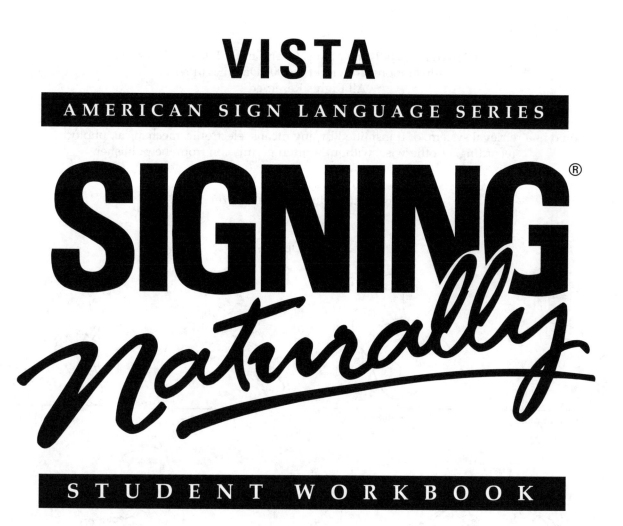

SIGNING® Naturally

STUDENT WORKBOOK

LEVEL

3

KEN MIKOS / CHERI SMITH / ELLA MAE LENTZ

SIGN ILLUSTRATIONS BY PAUL SETZER

DAWNSIGNPRESS
San Diego, California

Illustrations by Anna Bogri
Sign Illustrations by Paul Setzer

SIGN MODELS

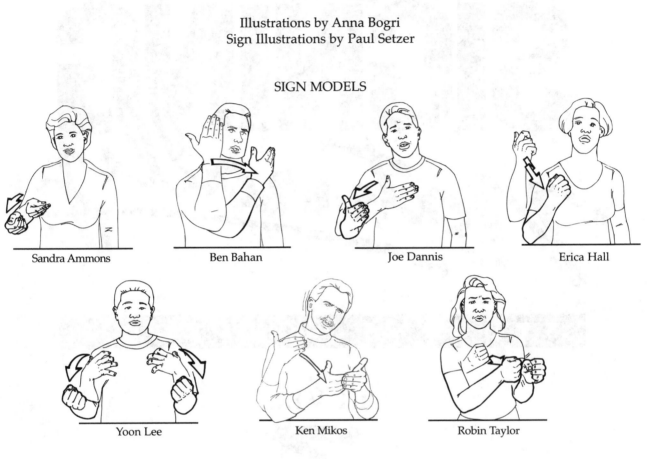

| Sandra Ammons | Ben Bahan | Joe Dannis | Erica Hall |

| Yoon Lee | Ken Mikos | Robin Taylor |

Published by DawnSignPress

ISBN: 978-1-58121-135-1

Printed in the United States of America

15 14 13 12 11 10

Attention: Schools and Distributors

Quantity discounts for schools and bookstores are available.

For information, please contact:

DawnSignPress
6130 Nancy Ridge Drive
San Diego, CA 92121

(858) 625-0600 V (858) 625-2336 FAX
(858) 768-0428 VP

VISIT US AT www.dawnsign.com

CONTENTS

INTRODUCTION

The Signing Naturally Level 3 Student Workbook and Videotext are designed to compliment course work in American Sign Language (ASL). These advanced materials help to increase your vocabulary, develop your everyday conversational skills, introduce you to translating written text into ASL, and improve your ability to make formal presentations in ASL.

Also included in your materials is a video called Signing Stories. Accompanying assignments in your workbook are designed to enhance your comprehension skills.

Student Workbook

The Student Workbook is used in the classroom, and also used outside the class along with the Student Videotext for additional study, review, and practice. The workbook is important and should be brought to each class.

The workbook has several sections:

Classroom Exercises

These exercises are used in the classroom as part of the lesson. The exercises are developed specifically to provide the opportunity to use grammatical feature(s) and rehearse new vocabulary you learned during the lesson. Your teacher will tell you when to open your workbooks to these pages.

Assignments

The assignments are usually video-related homework where you study specific video segments from the Student Videotext and complete accompanying materials in the workbook. Your teacher will let you know which assignments to complete and when they are due.

Review Notes

The review notes summarize the essential language features taught in the lessons. These are written notes explaining the specific language feature(s) that correspond to video examples.

Language Notes and Vocabulary Review

Many of the units also have Language Notes or a Vocabulary Review. These sections have sign illustrations that are often accompanied by a definition and an explanation of how to use the sign.

Guidelines

The narrative and presentation units (Units 18, 21, 24, and 25) conclude with guidelines for how to prepare the final presentation. Various notes about language are accompanied by corresponding video segments that show important aspects you need to include in your own presentation.

Sign Illustrations

Illustrations can never take the place of learning signs from an instructor or from interacting with signers. The illustrations in this book are here to help you recall the signs taught.

The basic four parameters of every sign are handshape, palm orientation, location, and movement. When evaluating a sign illustration, first identify how each of these elements contributes to the sign.

Because ASL is a visually active language the most difficult requirement of a sign illustration is to show movement. To facilitate the three-dimensional nature of signs, illustrations incorporate a number of helpful features.

Arrows show the direction, path, and repetition of the movement. Here are the arrows you will see.

Directional arrows point in the direction the sign is to be made.

Bi-directional arrows indicate a back and forth motion.

Path arrows show you the path of the sign's movement.

Repetitive arrows indicate that the sign's movement repeats twice or more.

A touch is when part of the sign touches the chest, shoulder, or other part of the body. Touches are shown with touch marks.

When a sign is supposed to be "wiggled" or moved back and forth slightly, there will be wiggle marks indicating this. Here are examples of wiggle marks.

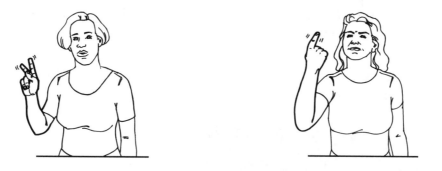

Some signs change location from beginning to end. In this book, line thickness is used to distinguish the beginning of the sign's motion from that at the end of the sign's motion. If the lines of the arms and hands are thin, they indicate the placement of the arms and hands at the beginning of the sign. If at a different place on the drawing the lines of the arms and hands are thick, they indicate the placement of the arms and hands at the end of the movement. Here are some examples of signs with movement indicated by line thickness.

If you are able to identify and evaluate the four parameters of a sign, your ability to use sign illustrations as a learning tool will be increased.

The Student Videotext

The Student Videotext contains video clips, segments, and narratives that correspond with assignments, review notes, and guidelines in the workbook. Other video examples are used for comprehension, rehearsing, and preparing to retell information in class.

At the beginning of each unit you will see on screen the unit, title, and kind of clip—as shown below.

To help you know which unit you are looking at, you will see the unit number in the bottom right corner. This is to help you search through the video more easily.

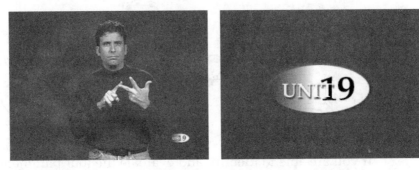

full screen   *close-up of unit number*

At the end of each video section, a white bar will cross the screen. That signals the end of the particular activity you are working on.

Remember these things when using the videotext:

1. All of the instructions for using the videotext appear in the workbook. Read all instructions in the workbook before starting any activity.

2. If you miss a sign or sentence while working on an activity, do not rewind the tape too often. This saves wear and tear on your tape.

The signers in the Student Videotext are identified by their actual names in the workbook. Here are the signers you will see in the videotext.

Ben Bahan

Byron Bridges

Ken Clark

Stefanie Ellis

Missy Keast

Marlon Kuntze

Cinnie MacDougall

John Maucere

Anthony Natale

Nikki Schmitz

Terrylene

SIGNING STORIES VIDEO

This video and the assignments that accompany it are meant to enhance your comprehension skills. The video includes eight signed stories or lectures on various topics that mostly relate to the Deaf experience.

The assignment for each story can be found in the Signing Stories section of your workbook, beginning on page 231. The assignments vary but include outlining a story, translating a story, answering questions for comprehension, answering questions for analysis, summarizing, paraphrasing and retelling. Your teacher will tell you when and how to complete the assignments.

Here are the signers you will see in the Signing Stories Video.

Laurene Gallimore

Marlon Kuntze

Cinnie MacDougall

John Maucere

Mary Telford

NARRATING UNFORGETTABLE MOMENTS

Sharing personal and amusing stories is one way people connect with each other. The ability to share stories is an important component in developing and maintaining relationships. Stories expand the conversations beyond everyday topics. Telling stories about unforgettable moments is sure to make others laugh, wince, or sigh in relief and is a good springboard for strengthening connections with each other.

Goal of the Unit

This is one of several narrative units designed to help you develop essential skills needed to tell a story successfully. Role shift is an essential tool used in telling anecdotes, stories, or even jokes. Role shift allows you to tell what happened in a vivid way, and it allows you the rich opportunity to describe the person's thought, behavior, or reaction simultaneously. Additionally you will learn to maintain spatial agreement between the location of people; sequence classifiers; time reactions to coincide with the action; and to elaborate on a story by giving descriptions, sharing thoughts, and giving reasons.

CLASSROOM

Exercise 1: Hit or Miss

Instructions   Follow the Basic Role Shift Sequence to develop the situations. For each situation, decide the other person's position and distance from you, choose one of the outcomes, and visualize the action sequence and the reactions a person would have in the given situation.

> **Basic Role Shift Sequence**
> 1. Tell where you and the other person are located.
> 2. Name the object.
> 3. Tell how the object is passed between the two people.
> 4. Possible outcomes
>   a. person catches the object
>   b. person drops the object
>   c. person is hit by the object
>   d. person sees the object just in time
>   e. person is nearly hit by the object

Situations   1. You toss an egg to another person.

2. You throw a screwdriver to a person standing on the roof of a house.

3. You throw a long football pass down field to a receiver.

4. You snap a knife with butter on the end at another person.

5. You throw a Frisbee to another person.

6. You swing your leg and your sandal comes off and flies toward the other person.

7. You are twirling a chain on your finger and it slips off in the direction of the person sitting beside you.

8. While you are signing you knock your glasses off and they fly toward the other person.

9. You spit your gum out the front window of a car and it is blown back in through the rear window toward the passenger in the back seat.

Basic Role Shift—Outcomes A–E

These video demonstrations build on your classroom knowledge and practice. The segments shown are designed to help you refine and practice your role shift skills and become more adept at timing reactions to coincide with the actions taking place.

Outcome A—Person Catches the Ball

View. View the video segment "Outcome A" to see how each part of the sequence below is addressed in the signed narrative.

> **Basic Role Shift Sequence**
> 1. Tell where you and the other person are located.
> 2. Name the object.
> 3. Tell how the object is passed between the two people.
> 4. Tell the outcome.

Video Notes. Following is a description of how each part of the sequence outlined above is signed.

1. Tell where you and the other person are located.

   Stefanie introduces and places the characters with raised eyebrows.[1] She shows agreement by glancing in the direction of the man when referring to him.

2. Name the object.

   Stefanie shifts to the woman and tells that the ball was thrown, fingerspelling "ball."

3. Tell how the object is passed between the two people.

   Stefanie shifts to the woman to show her throwing the ball and tracks the movement of the ball with her eyes as it travels toward the man located on her left.

4. Tell the outcome.

   Stefanie shifts to the man, changing her eye gaze and body orientation, and resumes tracking the imaginary ball from the man's point of view. The man's expression shows that the ball was caught with ease.

View. The segment will repeat, this time in *slow motion*. Watch for three things: use of role shift, raised eyebrows, and eye gaze.

---

1. Raised eyebrows and a slight tilt of the head are used to introduce a topic, to signal a change in the topic of conversation, to refer to a previously mentioned topic, or to emphasize the topic.

3

Outcomes B–E

In the remaining *four* video segments the story begins the same, but ends with a different outcome that requires the signer to use different expressions. You can review the information two ways. One way is to read the accompanying video notes for all four segments before viewing them. A second way is to stop the tape after each video segment and read the accompanying video notes.

View. The beginning of each video segment is shown at *regular speed*, but the different outcomes are shown in *slow motion.*

Outcome B—Person Drops the Ball

Video Notes. Stefanie shifts her body to show the man readying himself to catch the ball (open mouth in anticipation of catching the ball) and simultaneously shows the ball approaching with her right hand (LCL:S*"ball"*). When the ball reaches the man's hand, the signer changes her facial expression into "th" mouth expression meaning "clumsily" or "out of control" and continues that expression when showing the ball bouncing away.

Outcome C—Person Is Hit by the Ball

Video Notes. Stefanie shifts to show the man looking away using "th" expression indicating "inattentive" or "unaware" and simultaneously shows the ball approaching him with her right hand (LCL:S*"ball"*). The moment the ball hits the signer's cheek, she changes her expression from "being unaware" to "pain/anger" while her eye gaze shifts to the right to show the man looking to see who threw the ball.

Outcome D—Person Sees the Ball Just in Time

Video Notes. Stefanie shifts to show the man blinking as he turns his head to the right with an "unsuspecting" facial expression. Her expression changes to "surprised/panic" showing the man's reaction to the oncoming ball before making the catch. The moment the ball is caught, Stefanie blinks her eyes to indicate impact. When she opens her eyes, her head shakes showing relief.

Outcome E—Person Is Nearly Hit by the Ball

Video Notes. Again, Stefanie shifts to show the man looking away using "th" mouth expression indicating "inattentive" or "unaware." With her right hand she shows the ball coming using LCL:1*"direction of ball."* As the ball reaches the vicinity of the signer's face, she changes her facial expression from an "unaware" to a "surprised" reaction. The signer continues this "surprise" expression as she changes her eye gaze to show the man looking to see who threw the ball and at the same time her right hand, LCL:1*"ball passing,"* shows the ball going past the man's face.

For further discussion of locative classifiers (LCL), read the Language Notes on pages 23–24.

Rehearse Outcomes B–E

View. This time Outcomes B–E are shown at normal speed. After you have watched all of the outcomes, practice signing them, incorporating all the language elements discussed in this section until you can deliver a vivid yet fluid picture of the man's reactions to the situation.

CLASSROOM

Exercise 2: Oops

Instructions Follow the Basic Role Shift Sequence to develop the situations. For each situation, decide the other person's position and distance from you and visualize the action sequence and the reactions before, during, and after the situation occurs.

> **Basic Role Shift Sequence**
> 1. Tell where you and the other person are located.
> 2. Tell what the person is doing.
> 3. (Transition) Tell how the liquid is passed between the people.
> 4. Describe the result and the person's reaction.

Situations

1. As you're holding an infant, he throws up on you.
2. A bird flying above makes a deposit on your head.
3. Someone throws a cup of water on you.
4. A child sitting across the table from you bursts out laughing and soda comes flying out of his mouth all over you.
5. A dog urinates on your shoe.
6. While filling a cup, it tips over and spills into another person's lap.
7. The catsup isn't coming out of the bottle, so you hit it a few times on the bottom and it comes out all over the person next to you.
8. You bend over to see what a little boy has behind his back. Just as you get close he pulls out a water gun and squirts you in the face.
9. You are eating a grapefruit. You stick the spoon in and out comes a squirt of grapefruit juice into another person's eye.
10. Playing baseball, you call a guy out at first. He protests the call. While he is yelling he is spitting at you.
11. You are eating and your dog comes to beg for some food. He puts his head on your lap and begins to drool on your pants.
12. You drop a water balloon from the second floor of a building.

Exercise 3: How Did It Happen?

Instructions Follow the narrative sequence and practice signing each incident. For each incident, visualize the action sequence and consider the reactions before, during, and after the incident

---

Trip-Fall Sequence
1. Describe kind of barrier/surface (LCL).
2. (Transition) Describe the fall (SCL:V + reaction).
3. Describe the result of the fall and/or comment on the incident.

Incidents

1. It was damp outside. I was jogging along and saw a mud puddle. I jumped over, but slipped and fell in the mud. I hurt my arm trying to catch myself.

2. I was being careful not to walk too fast on an icy sidewalk, but ended up losing my footing, slipping, and falling.

3. I went down on my back on a water slide. I twisted, turned, and went through a tunnel that emptied out into a quiet pool of water. My back ached, but it was fun.

4. I slipped on the top step of some stairs that someone had been mopping and hadn't finished rinsing. I bounced down the whole flight of steps to the bottom. My buttocks were sore, but I was relieved no one saw me.

5. My friend and I were walking around a water fountain when she got the brilliant idea to splash water on me. I took off running but didn't get very far before I lost my balance and ended up falling into the fountain.

6. On a hike I came to a rushing river. To cross it I had to walk on a log. Halfway across, I slipped and fell. The river carried me along feet first for a bit. Finally, I managed to get out, coughing, wet, and scared.

7. As I was skiing down the last leg of the ski run I skied over a slight incline. I tumbled into a tree. My body ached all over.

8. Practicing a double axle in ice skating, I went up in the air, twirled, came down, fell, and twisted my ankle.

9. I was playing baseball. A guy hit a ball to right field. I ran to try and catch the ball but fell over the out field wall and landed on my elbow.

10. I was wearing a floor-length evening gown. As my date and I were walking up the steps to the dance, I tripped on my dress and tumbled down the stairs. As I got up, I felt dizzy.

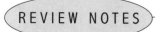

REVIEW NOTES

Role Shift —Initiator's and Receiver's View

In stories that describe physical contact between two individuals you need to role shift to both the initiator and the receiver, clearly showing how the contact was made.

The video demonstrations review how to describe situations involving physical contact from different points of view. Read the information for each demonstration before viewing the video.

Poke Ear

Initiator's View

View. Read the role shift sequence below and then watch to see how the man (initiator) tells what happened from his point of view.

Role Shift—Initiator's View
1. Tell where the other person (receiver) is.
2. Tell how you touched the other person.
3. Role shift to the receiver to complete the action.

Receiver's View

View. Read the role shift sequence below and then watch to see how the woman's version differs when she tells what happened from the receiver's point of view.

Role Shift—Receiver's View
1. Tell where the other person (initiator) is.
2. Tell how s/he touched you.
3. Show where you were touched.

Rehearse. Rewind the tape and replay both of the role shift sequences. In the first version, visualize the woman standing on your right as you tell about poking her in her left ear. Be sure to incorporate the initiator's reactions.

In the second version, visualize the man standing on your left as you tell about being poked in the ear. Remember to incorporate the receiver's reactions.

Poke Stomach

Initiator's View

View. In this segment the man (initiator) tells what happened when he poked the woman's stomach with his finger. Since the action involves a "push/pull movement," the woman stumbles back, represented by (2h)BPCL:1*"stepping back."*

Receiver's View

View. This segment gives you the woman's (receiver) view of the same incident. She establishes herself standing before shifting to the man poking her in the stomach and then shifts to herself stumbling back.

Rehearse. Rewind the tape and replay both segments. In addition to rehearsing the role shift sequence, pay special attention to using your eye gaze to further modify and agree with the actions taking place. Be sure that:

- when you tell the man's version, you direct your hand and focus your eye gaze in the vicinity of the woman's stomach while showing his mischievous expression
- when you tell the woman's version, you lower your eye gaze and track the hand of the man as it pokes you in the stomach.

REVIEW NOTES

Role Shift Variations A–D

You will review the four variations of role shift shown in class—three variations using the *Initiator's View* and one variation using the *Receiver's View*.

Read the information pertaining to the video segment, view the video segment, then re-read the video notes. Now replay the video segment and rehearse signing it before moving on to the next variation.

Variation A—Use Corresponding Gesture

Initiator's View. In this variation the signer role shifts to the receiver and uses a gesture to indicate where she/he was touched.

View. In this situation, Stefanie (initiator) tells about squeezing the man's (receiver's) nose. Read the role shift sequence below and then watch the video segment. Pay close attention to step 3.

Variation A—Use Corresponding Gesture

Initiator's View

1. Tell where the other person (receiver) is.
2. Tell how you touched the other person.
3. Use corresponding gesture (role shift to the receiver and use gesture in reaction to the touch).

Video Notes. In this variation, Stefanie role shifts to show the man (receiver) rubbing his nose implying his nose was squeezed. Stefanie states "his nose" before showing his reaction. By using "corresponding gesture," the signer's emphasis is on the receiver's reaction and less on how the receiver was actually touched.

Rehearse. Try repeating the segment now. Then try substituting "squeezing the man's nose" with a different situation like "slapping the man's face" or "poking the other man in the forehead." For each substitution, think of an appropriate "corresponding gesture" to use when you role shift the receiver (step 3).

Variation B—Show Receiver's Response

The second variation shows the receiver's response without role shift. In this case, the signer indicates that the receiver "turns and looks at" the initiator and then shows the receiver's reactions without shifting to the receiver.

"turning head to look at me"

View. In this video segment, observe how John (initiator) tells about pulling the woman's (receiver) hair. Read the role shift sequence, particularly step 3, and then view the segment.

Variation B—Show Receiver's Response

(Initiator's View)
1. Tell where the other person (receiver) is.
2. Tell how you touched the other person.
3. Show receiver's response (don't role shift to the receiver—instead indicate that the receiver turned and looked at you and indicate the receiver's reaction on your face).

Video Notes. In this variation since you do not role shift to the receiver to show where she was touched, it is necessary to name the body part touched before telling how the initiator touched it. In this segment, John states "her hair" before pulling it. To show the receiver's reaction without role shift John uses the sign "turning head to look at me (initiator)" and at the same time shows her reaction (peeved) on his face.

Rehearse. Follow up by rehearsing this segment. Try a few other reactions, for instance, puzzlement, surprise, or anger.

Variation C—Show Receiver's Change in Position

The third variation shows the receiver's change in position. When we tell about someone falling down or being pushed away, we do not usually role shift to the receiver to act out falling or stumbling back. Instead we use classifiers to describe the fall. For example:

fall forward

View. Stefanie (initiator) tells about pushing the man and shows how he fell. Review the role shift sequence, particularly step 3, and then watch the video segment.

Variation C—Show Receiver's Change in Position

(Initiator's View)
1. Tell where the other person (receiver) is.
2. Tell how you touched the other person.
3. Show receiver's change in position (don't role shift to the receiver—use SCL:V to show the changed position).

Video Notes. The signer does not role shift to the receiver, but uses SCL:V to show how the receiver fell. The focus is on how the receiver was made to change his/her position as a result of the contact.

In cases where you want to give more details about a fall you can use body or bodypart classifiers to describe what led up to the fall, e.g., (2h)BPCL:1*"stumbling"* or BCL*"trying to maintaining balance."*[2] (See notes on body and bodypart classifiers, page 26.)

Rehearse. Rewind the tape and replay the woman's version of what happened.

---

2. The symbol (2h) preceding the transcription for a sign means this particular sign is made with both hands.

Variation D—Show How Initiator Touched You

Receiver's View. In this variation instead of role shifting to the initiator to show how s/he touched the receiver, the signer remains as the receiver and shows where the contact was made.

View. John (receiver) tells about a woman approaching and tapping him on the shoulder and his puzzled reaction. Review the role shift sequence, particularly step 2, and then watch the video segment.

> **Variation D—Show How Initiator Touched You (without Role Shift)**
>
> (Receiver's View)
> 1. Tell where the initiator is standing or how she approaches you (use SCL:1"approach").
> 2. Show how the initiator touched you (while maintaining receiver's point of view).
> 3. Indicate your reaction.

Video Notes. In this variation John does not role shift to the initiator to show her actions. Instead, he uses the agreement verb "she to me" to show the initiator tapping him on the shoulder. In step 3, the receiver acknowledges contact by reacting with a puzzled facial expression and using the sign meaning "to look at the other person (see sign illustration page 11)."

Rehearse. Follow up by rehearsing the segment. Then try substituting "tapping on the shoulder," with a different situation like "kissing me on the cheek," "pulling my hair," or "pinching me." For each substitution, show how you reacted to the situation by using the appropriate facial expressions along with the sign meaning "turning head to look at."

A note on role shift and reciprocal verbs. If two people are acting in a way that is mutual and reciprocal, e.g., shaking hands with each other, hugging, or kissing, role shift is not used. In these cases, regardless of the point of view—initiator or receiver—the signer simply tells where the other person was and tells that they "shook hands," "hugged each other," or "kissed each other," without role shifting to the initiator (to begin the action) or to the receiver (to show receipt of the action).

Exercise 4: Unforgettable Moments

Instructions   Prepare to tell the stories by doing the following:

- organize the information in the story by visualizing the setting, location of the people, and the sequence of events
- act out the story with your partner to help you develop a fully elaborated story
- analyze the grammar elements needed, concentrating on the part of the story that is in boldface
- identify useful signs and appropriate conjunctions to talk about what happened
- elaborate on the story with descriptions, explanations, thoughts, and reactions
- add an introduction and conclusion to your story.

EXAMPLE

At a Little League baseball game, I was sitting on the benches watching the game. A stranger, mistaking me for someone else, excitedly approached me to hug and kiss me. I was a bit embarrassed, but I was more embarrassed for him.

Story 1   At the library, my boyfriend and I were browsing through shelves of books. After a while, feeling the need to be intimate, **I wrapped my arm around him, only to find that the person I hugged was a stranger.** My boyfriend had moved further down the aisle and another guy was standing next to me. My boyfriend saw what happened and busted up laughing.

Story 2   I was in another country where I didn't know the language. While I was standing near a water fountain a small boy, maybe 3 years old, wandered up and wanted a drink. I picked him up and held him over the fountain. **When I turned on the water, it came out with a great gush, splashing him in the face and soaking him.** He screamed. His mother rushed up angrily and grabbed him away. He was crying and she was yelling. I couldn't explain. Everyone was staring, thinking I had hurt this kid!

Story 3   I was walking through a cafeteria with a tray of food. I noticed this really cute guy. **Without watching where I was going, I slipped and fell, spilling food all over the floor.** My skirt flew up. To my horror everyone was looking at me. I got up, straightened my skirt, and, with my head hanging down, walked away quickly.

Story 4   One time, I went fishing with my friend and her brother. He had a brand new fishing pole. So I asked him if I could try it out. Well, **when I went to cast out the line, I ended up throwing the entire pole into the water.** Instead of fishing for fish, I wound up fishing for my friend's brother's brand new pole that was at the bottom of the lake.

Story 5   I bought this great key chain with a small metal case that holds things. One particular day my Dad came over to look at my car. I gave him the keys without thinking. **Somehow while working on the car the metal case opened and exposed something I didn't want my father to see.** We both looked at each other. He looked shocked and I looked helpless as I tried to explain the contents of the box. The more I explained the worse it sounded.

Story 6   My 4-year-old daughter and I were sitting on the bus across from an elderly man who didn't have any teeth—not even false ones! My daughter was staring at the man and then suddenly **she turned to me and, speaking quite loudly, asked "Why doesn't that man have any teeth?"** The man heard her and so did other people on the bus. I was so embarrassed. The man was sweet. He assured me that this was not the first time he'd heard that type of comment and then turned and asked my daughter how many teeth she had. Of course, my daughter proudly opened her mouth for him and all to see.

Story 7   While waiting for my friend to arrive at the airport, I decided I had to go to the bathroom. But the only women's bathroom in the area was closed, and I couldn't hold it any longer. My boyfriend suggested I use the men's bathroom and volunteered to guard the door. **While I was sitting in the stall, I noticed through the crack that a man had entered the bathroom and then left.** I waited a while to make sure no one was in the bathroom before leaving. Afterward , I bawled out my boyfriend for letting the man in. My boyfriend laughed saying he thought it would be funny.

GUIDELINES

Preparing Your Narrative: Telling about an Unforgettable Moment

Instructions Recall an embarrassing or unforgettable story that either happened to you or you happened to witness. The story must represent a situation from the following categories:

1. touching the wrong person
2. spilling/wetting something
3. falling
4. careless mistake
5. caught in the act
6. embarrassed by someone else

The story must have at least two characters. It can be a personal story, or a story about someone else. If the story is about someone else, make sure you know the story well enough to elaborate on it. The story should be between 3 and 5 minutes long.

Bring a high quality videotape to class. Check with your teacher about what length of tape to use.

Follow the narrative structure that follows as you prepare your story.

Narrative Structure

I. Introduction
  A. Create the context for the story. Include some of these:
     • description of the environment or description of the people
     • relationship of the people
     • time and place.
II. Body
  A. Describe the situation leading up to the incident.
     1. Elaborate on thoughts, behaviors, reactions, and feelings.
  B. Tell what happened.
     1. For the incident itself, use a role shift sequence.
     2. Time your reactions to coincide with the action.
     3. Use a transition.
     4. Tell the results.
III. Conclusion
  A. Frame the story. Include *one* of these:
     • what the person thought, learned, or resolved never to do again
     • what happened afterward
     • a general comment about the story itself.

Grading Criteria   The instructor will check your story for the following things and grade accordingly:

1. Body of the narrative
   - role shift was consistent
   - spatial agreement was maintained
   - classifiers were sequenced appropriately
   - reactions were well timed and appropriate
   - transitions were used appropriately
2. Overall narrative
   - cohesion: the story flowed logically from one part to the next
   - elaborations were sufficient to add color, texture, and dimension
3. Language fluency
   - use and range of vocabulary was appropriate
   - pacing was comfortable
   - presentation engaged the audience, signer was composed.

Prepare to tell a draft of your story on _____

(date)

Prepare to tell your final version of the story on _____

(date)

Review Narratives

Read through the Video Notes before watching the video segments. After you watch each segment, read the Video Notes again to see how the Basic Role Shift Sequence is addressed, to present the "Body" portion of the narrative.

Incident A—Involving an Object

To describe an incident involving an object, remember this sequence.

Basic Role Shift Sequence
1. Tell where you and the other person are located.
2. Name the object.
3. Tell how the object is passed between the two people.

View. Stefanie describes an incident involving missing a ball (repeated footage).

Video Notes

Tell where you and the other person are located.

Stefanie sets up the man on her left side using SCL:V *"man sitting over there."*

Name the object.

While role shifting to show the woman throwing the ball, Stefanie spells "ball," introducing the object.

Tell how the object is passed between the two people.

Here Stefanie shows spatial agreement between the two people and the ball. She role shifts to the man and shows him looking to his right and holding his hands up, anticipating the ball. However, the ball is dropped; thus the mishap. Stefanie shows it is an unexpected mishap by the facial expression "th" with protruding tongue.

For your story, remember to use an appropriate instrument classifier (ICL) to show how you pass the object to the other person and how they receive it. If the object is thrown, you can use a locative classifier (LCL) to trace the object's path. (See Classifier notes on pages 22–24 for further explanation.)

Incident B—Involving a Liquid

To describe an incident involving a liquid, remember this sequence.

> **Basic Role Shift Sequence**
> 1. Tell where you and the other person are located.
> 2. Tell what the person is doing.
> 3. (Transition) Tell how the liquid is passed between the people.
> 4. Describe the result or the person's reaction.

View. Nikki tells about an incident involving a boy and his water gun.

Video Notes

Tell where you and the other person are located.

Nikki establishes the spatial relationship between herself and the boy by establishing herself laying on one of the benches, and through role shift and classifiers shows where the boy is in front of her.

Tell what the person is doing.

Nikki role shifts to the boy showing him mischievously holding a water gun. She shows him moving around and looking up at Nikki as if plotting a prank. Then, she role shifts back to herself watching the boy climbing up the bleachers.

(Transition) Tell how the liquid is passed between the people.

Nikki uses role shift Variation D (see page 13) to show the boy holding the gun, squirting her, and the water splashing her face from her (receiver's) point of view. This is possible because the sign "to shoot" is an agreement verb that can show the initiator's actions without role shift. For her transition, Nikki uses a change in facial expressions. (See pages 29–30 for a list of transitions.)

Describe the result or the person's reaction.

This part begins with the quick mention of water splashing on Nikki's face and continues with Nikki's reaction (getting up quickly and bawling out the boy). Then, Nikki concludes with a description of the boy apologizing as he clumsily but quickly leaves the scene.

Remember if the liquid lands on another person, you must role shift to show where the liquid landed and how the other person reacted. (See page 23 for an explanation of element classifiers.)

Incident C—Involving Tripping and Falling

To describe an incident involving tripping and falling, remember this sequence.

Basic Role Shift Sequence
1. Describe the kind of barrier/surface (LCL).
2. (Transition) Describe the fall (SCL:V + impact).
3. Describe the result of the fall and/or comment on the incident.

View. This is an excerpt from Nikki's video story "Down Cactus Hill." The excerpt involves the scene where Nikki and her brother decide to take a shortcut back to the house and end up falling down part of a hill covered with cactus plants.

Video Notes

Describe the kind of barrier/surface (LCL)

In this excerpt the description of the barrier/surface is complex. Nikki at first describes the narrow path at top of the hill, then uses LCL:B*"path"* when describing her brother and herself starting to fall. Since this fall is lengthy, Nikki adds descriptions of the cactus plants (LCL:B*"parts of cactus"*) and how they broke off as she and her brother fell. Finally, she describes how they ended up on a ledge on the side of the hill (LCL:*"cupped hand on her weak hand with palm up"*). (See pages 23–24 representing barriers.)

(Transition) Describe the fall (SCL:V+impact)

Nikki describes this lengthy fall in parts. For each part where she establishes the various surfaces she uses SCL:V*"fall"* along with facial expressions to show the many impacts throughout the fall. Since this mishap involves *two* people falling, she uses SCL:V on *both* hands.

Describe the result of the fall and/or comment on the incident.

In Nikki's story, as a result of the fall, Nikki's and her brother's faces, arms and bodies were covered with sharp prickles from the cacti, causing some pain.

Remember to use facial expressions with SCL when describing the fall (see page 25 for facial expressions).

Incident D—Involving Touching Another Person

If your incident involves touching the wrong person, remember this sequence.

Basic Role Shift Sequence
1. Tell where the other person (receiver) is.
2. Tell how you touched the other person.
3. Role shift to the receiver to complete the action.

View. Byron tells how a girl came up to a man and smacked him in the rear only to realize she did not know him.

Video Notes

Tell where the other person (receiver) is.

In this video segment, Byron narrates from the point of view of the receiver. This is reflected in how he establishes the people in the story. First he explains where he was standing and what he was doing, then he sets up the girl approaching from behind and to the right of him.

Tell how you touched the other person.

Byron describes how the girl touched him. Byron role shifts to the girl to show her slapping him, then role shifts back to himself to show *where* on his body the girl slapped him (his buttocks).

Role shift to the receiver to complete your actions.

Byron doesn't show much reaction but rather emphasizes the girl's reaction and action—she is very embarrassed and walks away. In this video segment, Byron shows the girl *approach* and *leave* using semantic classifier SCL:1 with upright index finger.

Remember to determine the appropriate point of view (initiator or receiver) when describing a person touching or being touched by someone else.

LANGUAGE NOTES

Classifiers

Following is a discussion of the classifiers covered in this unit and some ideas on how best to use those classifiers in preparation for your story.

Instrument Classifiers (ICL). These classifiers show how a person handles/manipulates an object. These classifiers are usually used with role shift. In the illustrations below, the ICL handshape shows how a bouquet of flowers is held, given, and received with role shift.

ICL *"pass flowers"*　　　　　　　　　　　ICL *"receive flowers"*

In the illustrations below, the ICL handshape shows us the size and shape of the ball and, with role shift, how the ball is tossed and caught.

ICL *"toss"*　　　　　　　　　　　　　　ICL *"catch"*

If your story involves a mishap with an object, you may want to use ICLs to show how the object was handled leading up to and in causing an incident such as dropping a glass filled with water, mistakenly breaking a window with a bat, or gripping a rope to avoid falling into water.

Element Classifiers (ECL). These classifiers represent movements of "elements" such as air, smoke, water/liquid, rain, fire, and light. The two ECLs illustrated below describe a spill that splashed and a squirt.

ECL: S->5 *"liquid splash, spill, splatter"*

ECL: S->1 *"liquid squirted"*

If your story involves a mishap involving liquids, you will need to use ECLs to show where the liquid came from and where it landed. When showing where liquid landed you must role shift to the other person to show where the liquid landed and their reaction.

Locative Classifiers (LCL). LCLs tell the location of an object, and/or its movement. The description of movement is often accompanied by facial expressions to show the distance or the speed of the movement. For example, an object moving through the air "fast" is indicated by a low but level movement accompanied by an "oo" mouth and squinted eyes. An object "popped up into the air" is described with a high and curved movement accompanied by a slightly open mouth. The two LCLs illustrated below describe the path the ball takes in the air.

LCL:1 *"path of ball"* (fast)

LCL:1 *"path of ball"* ("pop fly")

Locative classifiers can be used to represent barriers. These LCLs refer to the shape and location of things that may cause someone to trip or fall: a rock, a rope, a banana peel, a toy, or a step. Different handshapes signify various objects: "C" hand with palm down usually represents things that are bulky, "B" hand with palm down represents things that are flat, and "1" hand with palm down represents things that are thin and/or long.

LCL:C *"bulk"*
"rock," "toy"

LCL:B *"flat"*
"flat surface," "step,"
"fence," "banana peel"

LCL:1 *"thin, long"*
"pencil," "rope,"
"wire," "bar"

If your story is about a trip or a fall, you may need to use LCLs to establish the barrier before explaining what happened.

Semantic Classifiers (SCL). In this unit semantic classifiers describe where the person is located, where they moved, and/or how they moved (with facial expressions).

The SCL handshape "vertical 1" illustrated below shows a person approaching and leaving a scene.

SCL: 1 *"approaching"*

SCL:1 *"leaving"*

The SCL handshape "V" is used to show the person's position: sitting, standing, lying, or standing on their head. This classifier is also used to describe falls. The direction of movement tells if the fall is forward or backward. The orientation of the hand tells where the person is facing: forward, sideways, or down.

SCL:V*"fall back"*

SCL:V*"fall forward"*

SCL:V*"lie on back, looking up"*

SCL:V*"sit facing me"*

Use these facial expressions with SCL to describe falls.

ahh

This expression indicates a person or thing is airborne or falling.

pow

This expression is used for both objects and people when there is impact.

Using these expressions allows you to tell what happen in a vivid way—which is essential to a well-told story.

Body Classifiers (BCLs). BCLs are primarily used to show how a person moves his/her arms, shoulders, or head. BCLs are always used with role shift. They are used to describe a person's actions. They can describe your own actions at a different *time* or in a different *place*. Only the upper part of your body "enacts" the verb of the sentence, for example, waving, shrugging shoulders, putting hands on the hips, or hitting the head in frustration.

Body Part Classifiers (BPCLs). These classifiers represent specific parts of the body in action. Actions of legs and feet in this unit are emphasized. To represent the action of legs, e.g., running, jumping, or crossing legs, use the BPCL handshape "X," "bent index fingers" (see below). Add facial expressions to describe how the person ran—easily, in a panic, or with determination. The BPCL handshape "B" represents the feet and toes and describes actions like tapping the floor, or wiggling the toes.

(2h)BPCL:X*"legs' actions"*   (2h)BPCL:B*"feet"*

In your story BPCLs can be used in combination with SCLs or BCLs to describe what happened with more visual appeal.

Descriptions of Injuries

To describe an injury, select the appropriate description from below. The following signs indicating a cut, bruise, or puncture can be modified to reflect where the injury is located. For example, if you have a cut on your face then the sign "cut" should be made on the face. If you have a cut on your arm then the sign "cut" should be made on the arm.

Cuts/Punctures

cut on the hand

puncture in the shoulder area with a small or pointed object

finger cut off

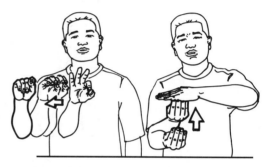

puncture in the foot with a sharp, flat object

Bruises/Lumps

bruise on the arm

lump on the forehead

Scratches

scratch on the face

several scratches on the face

Others

broken bones

burn on arm

To relay that a cut, puncture, or scratch results in bleeding add this element classifier.

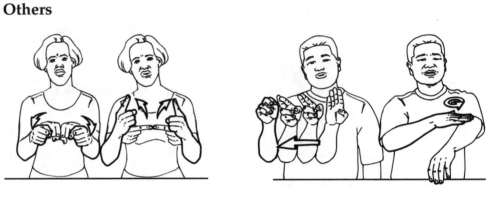

bleeding from forehead   *bleeding from elbow*   *bleeding from palm of hand*

Describing Injuries Outside of the Sign Space

BPCLs are used to describe an injury that occurs on a part of the body located outside of the signing space, such as an injury to one's foot or leg. To use BPCL in this way you first name the body part, use next BPCL to represent the part, and then show where the injury is. Either the hand, the fingers, or the arm is used to represent the body parts. For example:

fingerspell the body part	**use BPCL to describe the injuries**
• fs-LEG	Use BPCL*"forearm"* to show injuries between knee and foot
• *fs*-ANKLE	Use BPCL*"wrist"* to show injuries to the ankle
• *fs*-KNEE	Use BPCL*"back of hand"* to show injuries to the knee
• *fs*-TOE	Use BPCL*"finger"* to show injuries to a toe(s)
• *fs*-FOOT	Use BPCL*"hand"* to show injuries on the foot (see illustration page 28)

Note. For injuries to the back, spell out *fs*-BACK and then establish the "back" in the neutral space in front of you to describe the injury.

If the injury is on the face/head, torso, arm, elbow, or hands, then there is no need to name the body part. Just describe the injury to that body part.

Transitions   Use this sign to transition from an uneventful situation to one that becomes unexpected.

The signs shown below explain that the mishap was caused by a failure to notice warning signs and ends in an unexpected injury.

 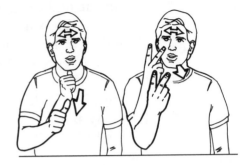

Superimpose this expression when signing what happened, e.g., fell, slipped, hit by a ball, etc.

SHARING INTERESTING FACTS

People find themselves wanting to relay in their daily conversations interesting or amusing information they have heard about or read. Interesting facts is the topic of this unit because these facts can be surprising, unbelievable, educational, and fun—the makings of an interesting conversation.

Goal of the Unit

This is the first of several translation units, designed to help you develop good interpretations of written information. Specific grammar structures are introduced to help you organize the essential information to show the relevance of the information presented. Because of the concise nature of each fact, you need to learn how to analyze the fact to understand what it means. When presenting the fact, you may have to explain, rephrase, demonstrate, or draw conclusions to convey the fact accurately. It is our hope that you will be better able to interpret written information into ASL without the interpretation being unduly influenced by English structure. We selected facts that fit into four categories: whole–part, listing, comparisons, and illustrating a fact.

CLASSROOM

Exercise 1: Whole–Part

Instructions Identify the *whole* and the *part* for each fact. Follow the translation guide to present the fact.

> **Translation Guide**
> 1. Set up the whole (use raised eyebrows).
> 2. Tell about the part using either percentages or fractions.
> 3. Contrast the part with the rest of the whole and add a comment.

Facts
1. 1 in 12 deaf children has deaf parents.
2. 1 in 9 teachers of the deaf is deaf themselves.
3. 1 out of 4 American Roman Catholics is Hispanic.
4. 1 out of every 10 restaurants in the United States serves pizza.
5. 57 out of 100 people on Earth are of Asian descent.
6. 1 out of 3 people in the world relies on rice for their survival.
7. 9 out of 10 new restaurants will not succeed.
8. 8 out of 10 boxers end up with some kind of brain damage according to the California Medical Association.
9. 1 man in 12 is color blind. 1 woman in 200 is color blind.
10. 49 out of every 50 tornadoes worldwide hit the United States.
11. Half of all muggings happen indoors—in hallways, elevators, and basements.
12. 40% of Americans say they dream in color. 23% of Americans say they dream in black and white.

For review see "Whole–Part," pages 41–44.

Exercise 2: Listing

Instructions   Determine the appropriate structure (A, B, or C) for each fact.

Discuss how to translate the underlined part of each fact.

Follow the translation guide to present the fact.

> **Translation Guide**
>
> A. Ranking
>   1. Establish the topic (use raised eyebrows).
>   2. Ask a rhetorical question to focus the topic.
>   3. List items by rank on your weak hand.
> B. Top five
>   1. Establish the topic (use raised eyebrows).
>   2. Ask a rhetorical question to focus the topic.
>   3. List items on the weak hand.
> C. Top, most, oldest
>   1. Establish the topic (use raised eyebrows).
>   2. List items on the weak hand.
>   3. Ask a rhetorical question.
>   4. Tell which is the top, most, or oldest.

Facts   ____ 1. The <u>best selling books</u> are, in order, the Bible, cookbooks, and books on <u>child-raising</u>.

____ 2. Which of the <u>four branches of the military service</u>, the Navy, the Air Force, <u>the Army</u>, or the Marines, <u>historically</u> has the highest <u>desertion</u> rate? The Navy.

____ 3. The <u>most common</u> dreams, according to researchers are, in order, (1) falling, (2) being chased or attacked, (3) <u>trying but failing to do some simple things</u>, (4) chores at work or school, and (5) sexual activities.

____ 4. What's the <u>most popular</u> name in the United States for 18-year-old men? Michael, <u>followed by</u> David, John, Joseph, and Jason. Jennifer tops the 18-year-old women's list, followed by Jessica, Nicole, Melissa, and Elizabeth (1991).

____ 5. In 1998, the five <u>most populous countries in the world</u> were, in order, (1) China with 1.22 billion, (2) India with 968 million, (3) the United States with 269 million, (4) Indonesia with 210 million, and (5) Brazil with 165 million.

_____ 6. In 1992, the most common <u>injuries</u> were (1) injuries involving people falling down on ramps, stairs, landings, and floors, (2) injuries <u>involving beds</u>, mattresses, and pillows, (3) injuries involving cleaning agents, and (4) injuries involving cigarettes.

_____ 7. The four <u>most popular "color" names</u> for dogs are Blackie, Midnight, Yellow, and Rusty.

_____ 8. Of these three men, Abraham Lincoln, Napoleon Bonaparte, and Winston Churchill, which has had more <u>biographies</u> written about him? The answer is Napoleon.

_____ 9. The worst complaints customers have about restaurants are (1) air hand dryers in the restroom, (2) room <u>temperatures too high or too low</u>, (3) <u>waiters paying more attention to other diners</u>, (4) <u>waiting too long for water refills</u>, and (5) <u>too small portions</u>.

For review see "Listing," pages 44–46.

CLASSROOM

Exercise 3: Comparisons

Instructions First analyze the fact by filling in the blanks. Follow the translation guide to present the facts.

> **Translation Guide**
>
> 1a. Name the topics being compared (use contrastive structure).
> 2a. Pose a question (use rhetorical question).
>   *or*
> 1b. Pose a question (use rhetorical question).
> 2b. Name the topics being compared (use contrastive structure).
>
> 3. Supply an answer.
> 4. Give interpretation by addressing either
>   • why it is true
>   • what should be done.

Use the example below to help you understand how to fill in the blanks.

Example

1. Babies of deaf parents learn to use sign language about 3 months earlier than babies of hearing parents learn to speak.

Topics	*babies of Deaf parents (DP), babies of hearing parents (HP)*
Question	*who learns to communicate first?*
Information	*babies of DP learn first, 3 months before babies of HP*
Interpretation	*the voice box takes longer to develop than hand movements, or, we should use sign language with all babies**

* There is no correct interpretation. As you formulate your interpretation, address either the reason why it is true or what should be done to change, prevent, or improve the situation.

2. There are more places and things named after Abe Lincoln (1,361) than places and things named after George Washington (1,346).

Topics	_____
Question	_____
Information	_____
Interpretation	_____

3. Every year in this country, more steel goes into bottle caps than into cars.

Topics _____

Question _____

Information _____

Interpretation _____

4. The movie industry employs 200,000 people. The auto industry employs about 3 million.

Topics _____

Question _____

Information _____

Interpretation _____

5. The alcohol content of beer and wine ranges from 3.2 to 14 percent. The alcohol content of the leading mouthwashes ranges from 14 to 27 percent. For this reason mouthwashes are banned in most prisons.

Topics _____

Question _____

Information _____

Interpretation _____

6. Country folk live an average of 5 years longer than city folk. Vegetarians live an average of 10 years longer than nonvegetarians do.

Topics _____

Question _____

Information _____

Interpretation _____

7. The male-female ratio in Anchorage, Alaska, is 107.7 men to 100 women. In Jackson, Mississippi, it's 88.3 men to 100 women.

Topics _____

Question _____

Information _____

Interpretation _____

8. Who gets kicked out of high school? Three times as many <u>students from one-</u>
    <u>parent families</u> as from <u>two-parent families</u>.

    Topics   _____

    Question   _____

    Information   _____

    Interpretation   _____

9. The <u>Las Vegas Hilton</u> has three times as many hotel rooms as has the whole
    <u>country of Burm</u>a.

    Topics   _____

    Question   _____

    Information   _____

    Interpretation   _____

10. Americans spend four times as much money on <u>pet food</u> as on <u>baby food</u>.

    Topics   _____

    Question   _____

    Information   _____

    Interpretation   _____

For review see "Comparisons," pages 47–51.

CLASSROOM

Exercise 4: Illustrate a Fact

Instructions　Fill in the blank with the general topic and the best possible question to pose for each fact.

Discuss how to translate the boldfaced, underlined parts of each fact.

Follow the translation guide to present the fact.

Translation Guide
1. Broach the subject.
2. Name the topic (use raised eyebrows).
3. Pose a rhetorical question.
4. Explain.

When deciding how to translate the whole fact, think about:
- which phrase you will use to broach the subject
- how role shift can help illustrate the point more clearly
- what kind of interpretation would make the point of the fact clear
- which nonmanual markers, rhetorical question or topic-comment, will help emphasize the point.

Facts　1. **The slit in the lower back of a man's suit coat** was originally designed for comfort on horseback.

　　　Topic: _____

　　　Question: _____

　　2. In a spider's web, **the circular threads are sticky and the spoke threads are dry. The spider always walks on the spokes,** so it doesn't get hung up in the web.

　　　Topic: _____

　　　Question: _____

　　3. A fellow named Muldoon, a Union commander during the Civil War, invented the shower **by perforating the bottom of a suspended bucket to let water run out.**

　　　Topic: _____

　　　Question: _____

4. The left half of your heart is much stronger and better developed than the right side. That is because **the left half has to pump blood through your entire body, while the right half only has to pump blood through the lungs.**

    Topic: _____

    Question: _____

5. The left eye of the squid is four times larger than the right eye. This lets him see better, though not look better. He **uses the little eye close to the surface and the big eye down deep.**

    Topic: _____

    Question: _____

6. Among cab drivers, more skin cancers show up on the left side of the face in the United States, on the right side in Great Britain. It's **the side most exposed to the sun while driving** in both cases.

    Topic: _____

    Question: _____

7. **Conjoined twins, rather than identical, are mirror images. One is right-handed, the other is left-handed. The scalp whorl on one turns clockwise, on the other counter-clockwise.** Internally, the organs such as **the liver will be on the right side in one, but on the left in the other.**

    Topic: _____

    Question: _____

8. The first known knee surgery performed occurred 2,600 years ago in Egypt. **A nine-inch screw was used to tie together the thigh and shin bones** of a mummified Egyptian priest named Usermontu.

    Topic: _____

    Question: _____

9. A baby is born with about 350 bones. As you grow older, **lots of these little bones grow together to form larger single bones.** The average adult has 206 bones in their body.

    Topic: _____

    Question: _____

10. It turns out that there is, indeed, an explanation of why Americans hold their table forks in their right hand even though their European ancestors held forks in their left hand. In Colonial times, everybody held their fork with their left hand. However, **revolutionaries switched the fork to the right hand, first as a secret signal to one another of their political leanings, eventually as a public proclamation.** Those loyal to the King of England found themselves in a curious spot. If they didn't want to be identified as enemies of the revolution they had to switch their forks from their left to their right hand.

Topic: _____

Question: _____

For review see "Illustrate a Fact," page 51.

_____

Source: The Grab Bag, S.F. Chronicle (for #1, 2, 3, 5, 6, 7, 8, 10) (other sources for #4 and #9)

Translating Facts

The facts presented for review are organized into the four categories covered in class, Whole–Part, Listing, Comparisons, and Illustrating a Fact. You learned that each category has a particular grammatical structure. Use these structures when preparing your own facts to share. Facts can be found in magazines, newspapers, and almanacs.

Read the information about each category before watching the video.

Whole–Part   Facts that contain phrases such as "one out of" and "half of all" fall under the Whole–Part category. Since the fact is essentially about the part, it must be distinguished from the whole to make the point.

Use this structure to present whole–part facts.

> ### Translation Guide
> 1. Set up the whole (use raised eyebrows).
> 2. Tell about the part using either percentages, fractions, or ratio.
> 3. Contrast the part with the rest of the whole and comment.

Fact 1: Fractions

View. John stating the fact that "1 out of 4 women is addicted to chocolate."

Video Notes. Since *women* constitutes the whole, it is established first, followed by the fraction ¼ to indicate the number of women addicted to chocolate. John further contrasts the part by saying the remaining ¾ of women are not addicted to chocolate. John raises his eyebrows to emphasize the numbers, followed by a slight pause before commenting on the fact. The manner in which you emphasize the number tells the listener that this is a rather large number or a surprisingly small number.

Note. When the fraction is ¼, ½, and up to ⅞, the palm of the hand faces the signer.

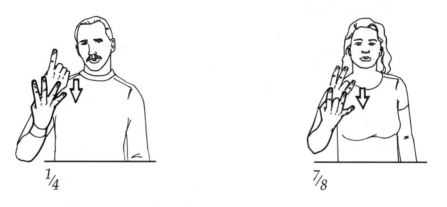

¼   ⅞

When the denominator is 10 or larger like ⅒, ³⁄₁₆, ⁷⁄₂₀, etc., the palm of the hand for the numerator 1-9 faces the listener.

¹⁄₁₀   ⁷⁄₂₀

Rehearse. Follow up by rehearsing this segment—use raised eyebrows when telling about the whole. Also, don't forget to raise your eyebrows to emphasize the numbers, followed by a slight pause before commenting on the fact. Try translating these sentences: "2 out of 5 men wear eyeglasses," "3 out of 10 women have shoulder-length hair." Remember to convert the numbers to fractions before signing the fact.

Fact 1: Ratio

View. Observe how John translates the same fact, this time using ratio.

Video Notes. To use ratio, John first identifies the whole "of all the women in the world," then sets up a hypothetical group (giving a number) to represent the whole, "4 women" on his left (weak) side. Then after telling how many in this hypothetical group John shows "1 woman" out of the group toward his right (dominant) side and makes the comment "is addicted to chocolate." This construction requires the use of a conditional clause, which makes it more complicated to follow and use.

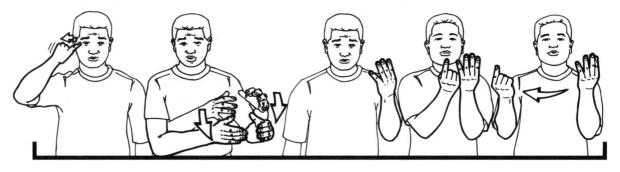

using ratio—"1 out of 4"

Ratio is used when the signer doesn't have time or doesn't know how to convert the data to percentages or fraction.

Fact 2: Percentage

View. Stefanie stating the fact, "8 out of every 10 books sold are paperback."

Video Notes. Stefanie begins with the whole "of all the books people buy," followed by the part, "80% are paperbacks." She contrasts this part by mentioning that the remaining books sold (20%) are hard covers. She uses contrastive structure to tell the part from the remainder. She emphasizes the numbers (80% and 20%) to help make the point. Stefanie ends by commenting on people's obvious preference for paperbacks.

Stefanie translates "books sold" by discussing the idea in terms of the number of books *bought*. By doing this, she focuses our attention on kind of books that the buyers chose, rather than emphasizing the kind of books the sellers chose to sell, which would have a different meaning than the one intended.

For percentages, we sign a number followed by this sign.

percentage

Rehearse. Follow up by rehearsing this segment using percentages. Remember to raise your eyebrows to set up the whole topic, use contrastive structure, and emphasize the number to help to make the point.

Fact 2: Ratio

View. Observe how Stefanie translates the same fact by using a ratio.

Video Notes. She begins with the whole, "of all the books people buy," followed by a hypothetical number, "for every 10 books that people buy," and then states how many of these books (8) are paperbacks. Stefanie points to the number on her hand to emphasize the number "8."

Rehearse. Take a couple of minutes to rehearse this segment using this emphasizing technique.

Listing

You have learned how to use listing to organize a fact. You can list by ranking, naming the top five, or naming the top, most, or oldest.

Ranking. Begin by establishing the topic, followed by a rhetorical question to focus the topic. Then, supply the answer by ranking the items on the weak hand in order.

> **Translation Guide**
> 1. Establish the topic (use raised eyebrows).
> 2. Ask a rhetorical question to focus the topic.
> 3. Rank items on your weak hand in order.

Fact 3: Ranking

View. John stating "The U.S. cities with the highest divorce rates are first Dallas, then Phoenix, then Houston."

Video Notes. John begins with the topic, "of all the cities in America," followed by the rhetorical question, "which city has the highest divorce rate?" Notice that he holds the rhetorical question for an additional beat, to focus the listener's attention on the answer that follows. Then, he holds up his weak hand (with the number 3) to list the cities, then signs "first place," points to the thumb, and fingerspells "Dallas," signs "second place," points to the index finger, signs "Phoenix," and finally signs "third place," points to the middle finger, then signs "Houston." He closes with a comment.

Use these signs to rank the items—first tell the ranking, then refer to the appropriate finger on the weak hand.

1st place (point to thumb on weak hand)

Rehearse. Now rehearse the video segment. Practice using this sequence when giving the answer in rank order—state the rank 1st, 2nd, or 3rd, then refer to the finger on the weak hand that corresponds to the ranking, then give the name of item.

Top Five. As you have seen, naming the top five suggests that there is no obvious order or ranking.

Translation Guide
1. Establish the topic (use raised eyebrows).
2. Ask a rhetorical question to focus the topic.
3. List on the weak hand.

Fact 4: Top Five

View. Stefanie stating "The five most common surnames in the United States are Smith, Johnson, Williams, Jones, and Brown."

Video Notes. Stefanie begins with a rhetorical question and follows with a listing of the five most common surnames on the weak hand. When she points to one of the fingers on the weak hand, her eye gaze shifts, looking briefly at the finger before giving the name. She ends the spelling of the name with a nod. Nodding is another way to emphasize the point.

Rehearse. Now rehearse this segment. In particular, practice shifting your eye gaze to the weak hand as you refer to each finger on the hand. If you have the time, slow down the tape to watch how she blends the letters in the fingerspelled names.

Top, Most, Oldest. In this way of organizing a fact first list the items and then state which one on the list is superior to the others, e.g., "the most," "the highest," "the tallest," "the oldest," "the top," etc.

> **Translation Guide**
> 1. Establish the topic (use raised eyebrows).
> 2. List on the weak hand.
> 3. Ask a rhetorical question.
> 4. Tell which is the top, most., oldest, etc.

Fact 5: Top, Most, Oldest

View. Watch John explain "Of the three flags—the British Union Jack, the French Tri-Color, and the U.S. Stars and Stripes—the Stars and Stripes is the oldest."

Video Notes. John begins by establishing the topic "three flags" then he lists the flags, raising his eyebrows as he points to a finger on the weak hand and tells the name of the country the flag represents. Notice how John reestablishes his weak hand after he describes a flag. When he is ready to give the answer, he first points to the whole list represented on his weak hand, as he asks the question "which of these is the oldest?" He gives the answer by pointing to the correct finger, repeats what is represented by the finger, and ends with the comment "aren't you surprised?"

Rehearse. Practice asking a rhetorical question. Remember to:

- point to the list of items on your weak hand and then
- nod when you point out the finger that represents the answer.

A common way to show that the member(s) of a category or domain are superior to others in the same category—"the highest," "the largest," "the oldest," "the longest"—is to use the following sign.

To translate "the most popular," or "the most common," use the above sign followed by fingerspelling the word "common."

Comparisons   When the fact is about comparing two things (topics), use *contrastive structure.*

Contrastive structure requires that you establish one topic in the space to your left and the other in the space to your right. When signing information about the topic on the left, all signed information about the topic must be signed in the space to the left as well. The same is true about the topic on the right—all information about that topic must be signed in the space to the right.

To translate a fact that compares two things, you can:

- name the topics and then pose a rhetorical question

or

- pose a rhetorical question and then name the topics.

Name Topics, Pose Question

Translation Guide
1. Name the topics being compared (use contrastive structure).
2. Pose the question (use rhetorical question).
3. Supply the answer.
4. Give an interpretation.

Fact 6: Name Topics, Pose Question

View. Watch Stefanie state that "Babies of deaf parents learn to use sign language about three months earlier than babies of hearing parents learn to speak."

Video Notes. Stefanie begins by naming the two topics "babies of deaf parents" (on her right side) and "babies of hearing parents" (on her left side), then asks the rhetorical question "which learns to speak first?" After she gives the answer by pointing to her right side, she repeats the topic and contrasts it with the other topic. She ends with an interpretation.

Pose Question, Name Topics. This time the comparison begins with a question.

Translation Guide
1. Pose the question (use rhetorical question).
2. Name the topics being compared (use contrastive structure).
3. Supply the answer.
4. Give an interpretation.

Fact 6: Pose Question, Name Topics

View. Observe how John interprets the same fact, this time beginning with a rhetorical question.

Video Notes. When John begins with a question followed by naming the topics, he repeats the rhetorical question before supplying the answer and ends with an interpretation.

Supply the Answer

In supplying the answer to facts in this category, use a comparative phrase to indicate how one is different from the other.

Examples:

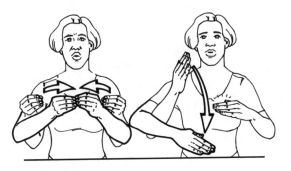

"more than..."

"less than... fewer than" (as if the scales have been tipped)

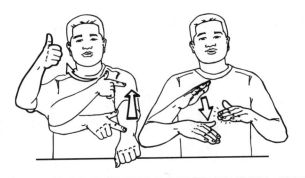

"longer than..."

"one occurring before the other"

"two times as much as..."

You can indicate "three times more than," "four times more than," and "five times more than" by using the appropriate number with the sign.

For numbers 6 or higher as in the phrase "six times more than another," use the phrase shown here.

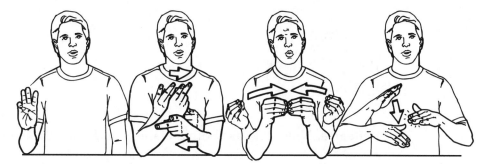

"six times more than..."

Give an Interpretation

Sometimes it helps to bring home the point of the fact, by giving your own interpretation of why the fact may be true or what the fact seems to imply. Rewind the videotape and replay both versions of Fact 6 again and see what interpretations Stefanie and John give.

Video Notes. Stefanie concludes Fact 6 by offering an explanation for why babies of deaf parents are able to communicate earlier. She suggests that using the hands is easier than using voice muscles at a very early age. Stefanie uses the sign below to transition into giving her interpretation. This sign is used when the interpretation is an attempt to give an explanation or offer a reason for the fact.

John concludes Fact 6 by commenting on the implications of the fact by saying that we should teach *all babies* Sign Language if we want them to develop communication earlier. John uses the sign below to transition into his interpretation. This sign is used when bringing out the significance or the implication of a fact. The interpretations are often posed as suggestions and sometimes as warnings.

Rehearse. Now rehearse both Stefanie's and John's versions.

Fact 7: Three Times More

View. Stefanie states "The Las Vegas Hilton has three times as many hotel rooms as the whole country of Burma."

Video Notes. Stefanie establishes the topics, Burma on her left, Las Vegas on her right, to compare/contrast them. She asks a rhetorical question and then gives the answer by pointing to the space representing the Las Vegas Hilton. She then uses a comparative phrase that further explains how many more rooms the Hilton has than the country of Burma.

Rehearse. Follow up by rehearsing this segment. Remember to use the comparative phrase when explaining the answer.

Illustrate a Fact

The final category in which we grouped facts are those that require the use of classifiers and role shift to clearly illustrate the fact. Recall some of the facts in Classroom Exercise 4 (pages 38–40) that used classifiers to describe things like "the slit in the lower back of a man's suit coat" or "by perforating the bottom of a bucket." Recall how you use role shift to demonstrate movement or behavior like "the squid using the big eye to see the bottom of the sea" or "switching the fork to the right hand." Now watch John use classifiers to explain the following fact.

Fact 8: Classifiers

View. John 's statement "In a spider's web, the circular threads are sticky and the spoke threads are dry. The spider always walks on the spokes, so it doesn't get hung up in the web."

Video Notes. John begins by describing the circular and the spoke threads of the spider's web; then shows how the spider travels on the spokes of the web. Notice how he broaches the subject by mentioning how surprised he was when he read the information in a newspaper.

Rehearse. Follow up by rehearsing the segment. Try to broach the fact differently, by mentioning that you had heard about it on the radio, heard it from a friend or teacher, or saw it on TV. Tell how you reacted to this information when you first heard it.

EXPLAINING RULES

In our daily lives, we often find reason to discuss rules. They can be rules we live by such as driving rules, societal rules, cultural rules or school rules; or they can be the rules we play by such as rules for party games, card games, or children's games.

Goal of the Unit

You will learn to give clear instructions or explanations using classifiers and conditional sentences, rhetorical questions, and relative clauses. You will learn rule-related vocabulary needed to achieve this goal. You will develop strategies for explaining rules while playing a game and learn to use attention-getting behaviors to manage a group during a game.

Exercise 1: Driving Rules

Instructions   Use this sequence to help you translate the driving rules listed below.

> **Driving Rules Sequence**
> 1. Describe the situation (use a conditional clause[1]).
> 2. Give the rule (use rule vocabulary).

1. You must have your driver's license with you whenever you drive.
2. To turn left, you must first give the right-of-way to all oncoming vehicles close enough to be dangerous before making the turn.
3. If you are driving in the fast lane, move to the right when another driver is close behind you and wishes to pass.
4. The driver of a vehicle cannot wear a headset, or earplugs, or talk on a handheld phone while driving.
5. You must turn your lights on any time you can't see at least 1000 feet ahead.
6. Dim your lights by switching to low beams before you are 500 feet from a vehicle coming toward you.
7. Don't drive in the blind spot of another driver.
8. When two vehicles meet on a steep one-lane mountain road where neither can pass, the vehicle facing downhill must back up until the vehicle going uphill can pass. (The driver going downhill has the greater amount of control when backing up.)
9. When you see or hear an emergency vehicle, pull as close to the right edge of the road as possible and stop until the emergency vehicle(s) has passed.
10. Bicycle operators and passengers under 18 years of age (including children in attached bicycle seats or in towed trailers) shall wear a properly fitted and fastened bicycle helmet.
11. It is illegal to drive with a blood alcohol concentration (BAC) that is 0.08% or more.

Source: 1998 California Driver Handbook

---

1. A conditional clause expresses a hypothetical situation, which is reflected by raised eyebrows, widened eyes, the head tilted slightly to the side and ends with a pause and eyeblink before the signer proceeds.

Rules We Live By

You have seen how, in ASL, rules are explained by first describing the situation with a conditional clause, then explaining what is required, permitted, or forbidden.

Read the information for each set of rules before watching the video segments.

Driving Rules   You have learned how to explain and discuss the signs and symbols of the road, speed limits, right-of-way, and personal safety. Review the structures for explaining driving rules.

Rule 1—A Yellow Flashing Signal Warns You to Slow Down and Proceed with Caution

View. Stefanie follows this sequence to organize the information.

Sign/Symbols

1. Identify the sign or symbol on the road.
2. Explain what it means.

Video Notes. Stefanie uses a conditional clause (raised eyebrows) to establish the yellow flashing light. Then she explains what the flashing light means by utilizing role shift to show how one should behave—in this case, slow down and check to see if the road is clear before crossing.

Stefanie begins her explanation of what the yellow flashing light means with this phrase.

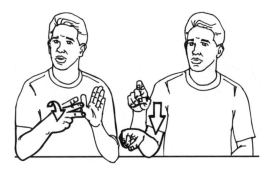

If the road sign/symbol prohibits one from doing something, e.g., "don't drive on or over a double yellow line," "no U-turn," etc., use this phrase to begin the explanation.

Rule 2—When Towing a Vehicle, the Maximum Speed Limit Is 45 m.p.h.

View. John follows this sequence to organize the information.

Speed limits

1. Describe the situation.
2. Explain what the speed limit is.

Video Notes. John describes the situation by using a conditional clause to pose a hypothetical situation "suppose you were towing." Then he explains the speed limit by using the rule phrase below. Fingerspelling "MPH" means "miles per hour."

John uses this rule phrase to state the required speed limit.

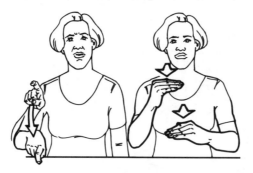

required to be limited

John elaborates on the rule by cautioning that going over the limit is not allowed. He uses the rule phrase below.

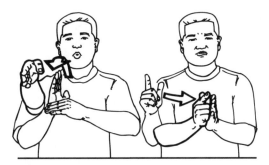

going over the limit is against the law

Another sign related to limits that is used in discussing rules about speed is shown here.

below the limit, under a certain number, less than a specified amount

Rule 3—When Riding a Motorcycle, Always Wear a Helmet

View. John emphasizes that when riding a motorcycle wearing a helmet is required in California. John follows this sequence to organize the information.

> **Personal safety**
> 1. Describe the situation.
> 2. Explain what you should or should not do.

Video Notes. John poses a hypothetical situation by saying "if you want to ride a motorcycle." He uses the rule sign that follows to explain that a helmet is required. He prefaces his statement by pointing out that the rule applies in California.

must, required

Rule 4—Yield to the Car on Your Right If It Has Reached the Intersection at the Same Time as Your Car

View. Stefanie follows this sequence when discussing a right-of-way rule.

Right-of-way
1. Describe the situation.
2. Ask a rhetorical question "who has the right of way?"
3. Give an answer.

Video Notes. Stefanie describes the situation by stating a hypothetical situation, "suppose two cars arrive at the intersection at the same time," and then poses a rhetorical question asking who should be the first to cross the intersection. When she gives the answer she emphasizes that the car on the right should go first.

Everyday Rules   You have learned that we use signs that vary along a continuum when we advise or instruct other people about rules that pertain to conduct or behavior. Depending on the kind of relationship we have with the other person, and the reason the rule or warning is being stated, our tone can be authoritative or diplomatic.

Use these signs to tell a person what s/he *should* do.

authoritative I——————————————————I *diplomatic*

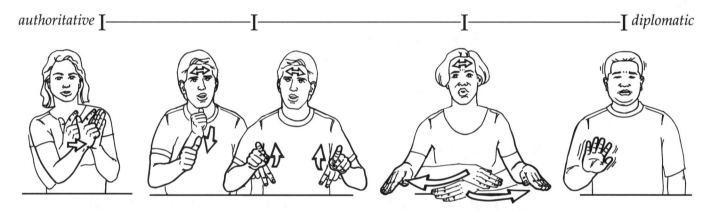

used if you don't have any other choice   *used if you have other choices*

Use these signs to tell a person what s/he should not do.

authoritative I————————I————————I————————I *diplomatic*

All four signs mean that something is not allowed. Choose the sign that fits the relationship you have with the person and fits the situation. Your choice should reflect the degree of directness and the amount of authority you are comfortable using.

Situations Requiring Immediate Responses

In situations requiring immediate response or compliance with a rule, the signer makes his/her signs brief and abrupt and superimposes a look of anger, frustration, or urgency depending upon how the signer perceives the other person's actions, e.g., careless, naive, or too slow.

The following signs, with the appropriate facial expressions, are a few examples of how to express your sense of urgency, frustration, or anger:

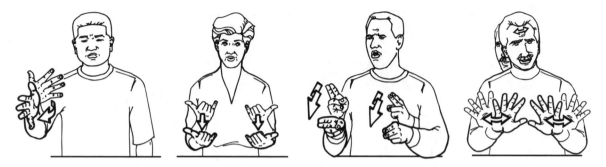

Rules 5–8

View. For video examples of Rules 5 through 8, the signers first show how to state the rules in ordinary situations. Then they repeat the same rule, this time showing how to state the rule in a situation requiring immediate response.

Rule 5—Talking Is Not Allowed in Class

Rule 6—Quiet after 11:00 P.M.

Rule 7—No Running Around the Pool

Rule 8—Passengers Are to Check in at the Gate 20 Minutes Before Departure

Video Notes. Notice how the signers' first explanation of a rule shows a relaxed demeanor and a more complete explanation. The second time the signers state the rule no explanation is given. Instead, their signing is short and abrupt and stated as a command—with an added sense of urgency, anger, or frustration.

Cultural Rules To explain the rules and customs of a culture, use a conditional clause to set up a hypothetical situation and then explain behavior that is appropriate or inappropriate.

Use these signs to describe *appropriate/inappropriate* behavior.

appropriate, acceptable   inappropriate, unacceptable

The next three video examples show the signer explaining the appropriateness of certain behaviors in one culture and then contrasting them with how they are viewed by another culture. Notice the signs used to discuss behavior.

Rule 9—Public Display of Affection

View. Stefanie compares the appropriateness of holding hands as a public display of affection in the United States and in Japan.

Rule 10—Showing Respect to Elders

View. John compares the appropriateness of children making eye contact with elders as a show of respect in China[2] and in the United States.

Rule 11—Interpretation of Burping

View. Stefanie discusses how people in Arab countries and in the United States interpret burping at the end of a meal.

Cultural Customs

In the next two examples, the signer explains how people in two different cultures say good-bye and schedule workdays. The following sign is used to denote behavior that is typical or common.

This sign can be one-handed or two-handed.

---

2. John uses one of the newer signs for China. Since the early 1990s, this sign has become widespread in America.

Custom 1—Typical Workday

View. Stefanie explains how people in the United States and in Spain[3] have different ways of scheduling a typical workday.

Video Notes. Signers use contrastive structure to establish two groups when comparing two cultures, one "here" and the other "there." Signers reference the group by referring to the space designated to discuss appropriate behavior for that group. These two signs are used to designate the space. If you review earlier segments you will see signers using the same signs to reference the two groups.

"in the present location," "here"

"away from here," "over there,"
"there in (place)"

Custom 2—Saying Good-byes

View. In this example, John compares the ways Deaf people and hearing people say their good-byes.

Video Notes. John uses a different contrast strategy to discuss two groups of people in the same country. To contrast the two groups of people in the United States, John uses space to the left and right of him to represent Deaf and hearing people. Then he references these spaces to contrast how each group says good-byes. John uses the sign below as a transition to describing how that behavior manifests itself in the second group.

---

3. There are several different signs for Spain, one of which is shown in the video. The sign Stefanie uses is common in Europe and has recently gained favor among the younger generation in America, especially those who have traveled to Europe.

Explaining a Card Game

Instructions To prepare for class, think of two or three card games you are familiar with. Review the rules for each game. Organize the rules for your game according to the outline below.

> 1. How the game is set up.
> 2. How the game is played.
> 3. How the game is won.

War

View. Review the grammar structures and card vocabulary. Then watch how John describes the position of the players, how to set up, how to play, and how to win (the card game "War").

Rehearse. Practice explaining your card games. The following guide suggests ways of organizing and explaining your game.

> 1. How the game is set up.
>   Make the position of players and card arrangement clear using LCLs, ICLs, and spatial agreement.
> 2. How the game is played.
>   Set up hypothetical situations to help you explain the rule(s). Use conditional clauses.
> 3. How the game is won.
>   Use a rhetorical clause to explain how someone wins.

As you imagine yourself explaining your game to your classmates, think about:
- how much to explain before, during, and after playing a round
- what is better explained by playing or by example
- what vocabulary or classifiers you will need to use
- when to look at each player to check comprehension before proceeding with the explanation.

Card-Related Vocabulary
Face Cards

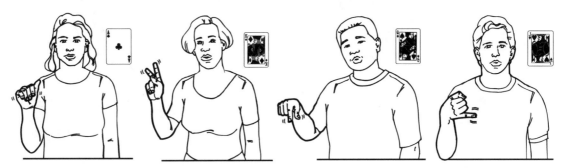

Suits of Cards

"Explaining a Card Game"

Note: *back and forth movement shows dealing between two people; a circular movement shows dealing to a group of people*

to hold hand of cards

to turn card face up

to take card(s) from

to give turn to person of the left

*to run out of (all cards),
to get rid of (all cards)*

to win the game

to lose the game

ASSIGNMENT

Explaining a Group Game

Instructions This assignment involves learning the game "Lady, Tiger, or Camera." Learn the game well enough to be able to explain the game next class.

Lady, Tiger, or Camera

View. Watch Stefanie explain how to play the group game.

Watch the segment again and analyze how Stefanie explains the rules of the game. Answer the questions below to focus your analysis.

1. How the game is set up.

   How is the arrangement of players described?

2. How the game is played.

   How is the information sequenced?

   How are contrastive structure, conditional clauses, and rhetorical questions used to explain the rules?

3. How the game is won.

   How does she use a rhetorical question to explain the concept "the team with the most points wins?"

Rehearse. Practice using Stefanie's instructions. Pay attention to where raised eyebrows and head tilt are used to signal different types of sentence structures.

Imagine yourself trying to explain this game to a group. Think about:
* where is the best place to stand to explain the game
* what parts of the game are better explained before the players take their positions
* what is better explained by playing or doing
* how to hold the group's attention throughout your explanation.

Group Game-Related Vocabulary

captain or leader

point(s)

Line up facing away from the teacher

Line up facing the teacher

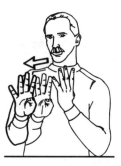

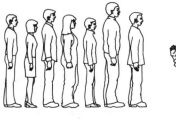

Line up in a row facing the teacher

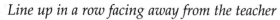

Line up in a row facing away from the teacher

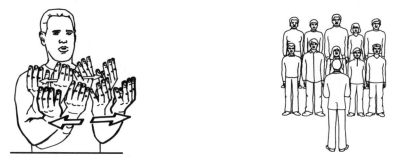

Make two lines, the front of each line facing the teacher

UNIT

21

TELLING ABOUT ACCIDENTS

We all have a story to tell about our misadventures, incidents involving a horse or a bicycle, car accidents, or even a near miss. These tales can engage and fascinate the listener; they can amaze or they can enlighten and guide us in making wise decisions the next time we encounter the same situations. Telling stories like these is a way of sharing our personal experiences with other people. The tricky part is learning how to describe the basic action, time reactions, and show different perspectives.

Goal of the Unit

This is another narrative unit designed to help you develop essential skills for telling a story successfully. You will learn to use more complex combinations of classifiers to tell what happened. For instance, talking about an incident with a horse usually requires switching between different classifiers used to represent the horse, the rider, and maybe a barrier. The same is true for telling about an incident with a bicycle or a car. You will also learn to time your reactions to coincide with the impact of a fall or an accident.

CLASSROOM

Exercise 1: Horse Incidents

Instructions   Follow the sequence and develop a narrative for the following situations.

> **Narrative Sequence**
> 1. Describe the situation
> 2. Tell what happened
>   a. Establish movement agreement
>   b. Reestablish the rider to show change in position
> 3. Tell the result of the incident

Situations
1. When I mounted the horse, it started to buck, throwing me forward off its back. I landed in front of the horse.

2. I rode all morning and decided to stop and rest. Once rested, I mounted the horse to continue my ride but the horse wouldn't budge. I tried everything, snapping the reins, kicking, yelling but nothing worked. So I tried slapping the horse's rear with my hands. The horse suddenly sat down and wouldn't get up until I got off.

3. I was riding along, when the saddle began to slip. Before I knew it, I slid off the side of the horse onto the ground. The horse continued a short distance then stopped to graze.

4. I kicked the horse several times trying to get it to go faster. All of a sudden, the horse put its ears down and took off in a full run. Ahead of us was a pond. The horse came to a dead stop at the pond's edge, catapulting me over its head into the water.

5. I was riding along when the horse decided to head for a tree. I tried to steer him away from the tree but the horse insisted on continuing the way he was going. The horse ran too close to the tree, causing me to scrape my arm and leg. I let go of the reins and fell off. The horse took off for the barn leaving me to walk back.

6. I was riding along and the horse and I were rounding a bend. I didn't see the low tree branch in time, and was knocked off.

7. The horse decided to jump a fence to get home quicker. Realizing what the horse intended, I quickly leaned forward, put my arms around the horse's neck and held on. When the horse landed, I was bounced onto the horse's rear end and held onto the saddle until we reached the barn.

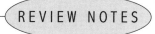

REVIEW NOTES

Describing an Incident with a Horse

When discussing horse incidents you have learned to follow this narrative sequence.

> **Narrative Sequence**
> 1. Describe the situation
> 2. Tell what happened
>   a. Establish movement agreement
>   - same speed
>   - change in speed
>   b. Reestablish the rider to show change in position
>   - no barriers
>   - with barriers
> 3. Tell the result of the incident

What follows is a review of what is included in each part of the narrative sequence.

1. Describe the Situation

Create a context for what is about to happen. For example, a friend who has never ridden a horse wants to try it, so two friends decide to go horseback riding.

2. Tell What Happened

a. establish movement agreement between the rider and the horse

- same speed (see Classifier Sequence 1, p. 75)

  If the horse's speed remains the same until the incident, use this classifier sequence:

  —show movement of horse using (2h)SCL:V*"horse legs"*;

  —show rider on horse using SCL:V*"rider"* on LCL:B*"horse"*;

  —show rider's actions using ICL*"hold reins."*

  Use the same facial expression for the speed throughout the sequence

- change in speed (see Classifier Sequences 1 and 2, p. 75)

  If the horse's speed changes before the incident, follow this sequence:

  —repeat the classifier sequence to establish the original speed;

  —reestablish the horse's movement (2h)SCL:V*"legs"* and show how abruptly or gradually the speed changed;

  —change facial expressions to reflect the new speed.

b. **Reestablish the rider to show change in position (this is where you describe what happened)**

- no barrier

  —Use a transition sign to indicate that what is about to happen next is unexpected

  —reestablish the person on the horse, then describe the person's fall or change in position on the horse using SCL:V*"person"*;

  —time the "ahh" or "pow" expressions with the action;

  —use BCL or BPCL to describe how the person ended up

- with barrier (see Classifier Sequence 3, p. 76)

  —Use a transition sign to indicate that what is about to happen next is unexpected;

  —name the barrier and establish it using DCL or LCL;

  —show the relationship of the horse to the barrier;

  —reestablish the person on the horse and then describe the person's fall or change in position on the horse;

  —time the "ahh" or "pow" expressions with the action;

  —use BCL or BPCL to describe how the person ended up.

3. Tell the result of the incident

To conclude the story describe reactions and injuries, and tell what happened to the horse and the rider after the incident. End the story with a comment.

"A Horse Incident" by John

Read the information pertaining to the video segment, view the video segment then reread the video notes.

View. This video segment is about John and his friend, who had never ridden a horse, going to a riding stable. John, being a bit of a show-off, told his friend to watch and learn. John's off-hand manner sets him up for an embarrassing moment.

Video Notes. This incident involves no change in the horse's speed and no barriers. Given this, notice how the information is organized and how the classifiers are sequenced and reactions timed. Pay attention to how John establishes movement agreement between him and the bucking horse by using (2h)SCL:V to describe the horse's bucking. His mouth movements rhythmically correspond with the action described and he maintains the expression throughout the sequence. When he's about to describe the fall, he reestablishes himself on the horse before telling us he went flying through the air using the "ahh" expression.

Rehearse. Follow-up by learning to sign John's description of the horse incident. Be sure to use facial expressions with the sequence of classifiers and to time the "ahh" and "pow" expressions with the fall.

Below are examples of the classifier sequence for review.

Classifier Sequence 1

establish movement agreement

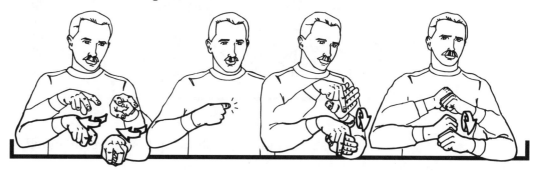

Classifier Sequence 2

show change in speed redundant

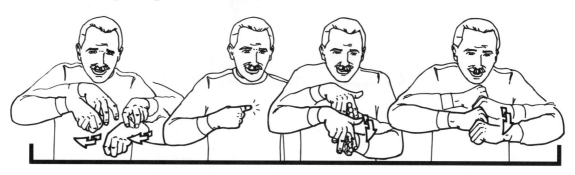

Classifier Sequence 3

describe barrier, reestablish horse to describe change in speed/movement

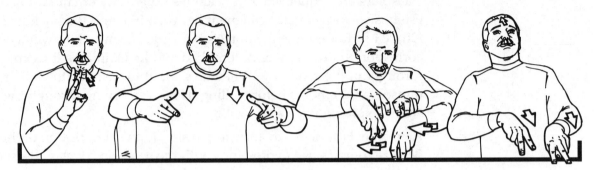

reestablish rider before describing fall

establish ground before showing how person landed

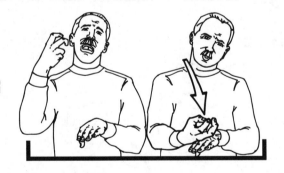

Essential Classifiers

Classifiers Used to Represent a Horse

This semantic classifier, (2h)SCL:V, is used to show the horse's position such as standing and laying or the horse's movement such as trotting, bucking, running, and jumping.

This is a combination of two classifiers—semantic ("V" representing a person) and locative ("B" on the weak hand representing the horse). This combination is used when describing a person straddling something, in this case a horse. The combination is used to show the interaction between the rider (SCL:V) and the horse (LCL:B), e.g., the rider bouncing on the horse and the speed at which both the rider and the horse are moving. The only time the horse is represented by the "B" handshape is when you talk about the rider on the horse.

This locative classifier is used to describe the direction or route the horse takes, e.g., the horse is running down the road or around the arena.

Classifiers Used to Show How a Rider Manipulates a Horse

This instrument classifier, (2h)ICL, is used to show a person holding or handling something, in this case holding the reins, pulling back on the reins, slapping the horse with the reins, or holding the horse's mane.

This bodypart classifier (2h)BPCL:X is used to represent legs. It can be used to describe the rider kicking the horse with both legs.

This body classifier, BCL, is used to "enact" the actions of a person, in this case, slapping the horse's rear end. This is distinguished from the other hand "holding" the reins, which indicates an instrument classifier (ICL).

Facial Expressions and Head Movements

Use this expression along with gentle head bobbing movements to indicate a leisurely ride on a trotting horse.

This expression requires repeating an open-closed mouth expression along with pronounced bobbing head movements to indicate a rough ride on a bucking horse.

Use this expression along with head thrust forward to indicate a fast ride such as one on a runaway horse.

Classifiers Used to Describe Incidents Involving Barriers

Descriptive classifiers (DCL) are primarily used to describe the size and shape of barriers. A LCL classifier is used to represent the barrier when describing what happened.

Follow this structure to describe incidents involving barriers.

1. Name the barrier
2. Describe the barrier
3. Describe the accident

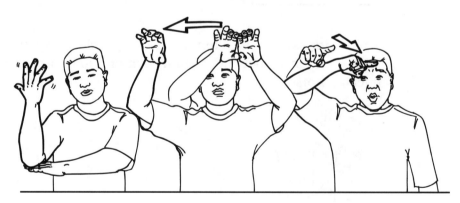

barrier: tree limb

barrier: fence

barrier: pond

Facial Expressions for Falls/Impact

This expression indicates that an object or a person is airborne. You could have the horse stop suddenly in front of a pond and have the rider flying through the air ("ahh") then landing on the ground ("pow").

"ahh"

This expression is used for both objects and people, whenever you have impact. For example, a person falls and lands on the ground—describing the moment of impact requires the "pow" expression.

"pow"

Transition Sign

This transition sign indicates that what is about to happen is unexpected. See page 30 for other useful transitions.

Useful Sign

This sign is used when a person or an animal, with a mind of its own, refuses to do something. In John's story, John states that his friend would not get on a horse even after John's reassurances that everything would be fine.

Exercise 2: Bicycle Incidents

Instructions　　Follow the sequence and develop a narrative for the following situations.

> **Narrative Sequence**
> 1. Tell what the person was doing on/with a bicycle
> 2. Tell what happened
>   a. Describe the barrier/terrain
>   b. Tell how the bicycle hit the barrier/terrain (impact)
>   c. Reestablish the rider to show how s/he fell and landed (reactions)

Situations
1. A bicyclist runs into a curb.
2. A bicyclist runs into an opening car door.
3. A bicyclist slips/skids on an oily or icy surface.
4. A bicyclist hits a wall or fence.
5. A bicyclist hits a bump or a dip.
6. A bicyclist hits the root of a tree.
7. A bicyclist hits a chain.
8. A bicyclist hits another person.
9. A car stops suddenly and a bicyclist hits the car.
10. A bicyclist loses control of his bicycle (for some unknown reason).

Describing an Incident with a Bicycle

When discussing bicycle incidents you have learned to follow this narrative sequence.

Narrative Sequence

1. Tell what the person was doing on/with a bicycle
   a. bicycle trick
   b. bicycle stunt
   c. two people on a bicycle
2. Tell what happened
   a. describe the barrier/terrain
   b. tell how the bicycle hit the barrier/terrain (impact)
   c. reestablish the rider to show how s/he fell and landed (reactions)

What follows is a discussion of how to organize the information for each part of the narrative sequence.

1. Tell What the Person Was Doing on/with a Bicycle

Review how to sequence the information when describing a bicycle trick, stunt, or incident involving two people on a bicycle.

a. Bicycle trick (change in the rider's position)

- Establish person riding a bicycle
- If a trick involves part of the bike such as the handlebars, seat, or crossbar, describe using a DCL

- Describe the rider's changed position
  —If the change involves the whole body, use SCL:V, e.g., laying prone, sitting sideways on the crossbar, sitting on the fender, kneeling on the seat.
  —If the change involves holding on to other parts of the bicycle, use ICL, e.g., holding the crossbar, back of the seat, or riding without hands.
  —If the trick involves the feet or legs only, use (2h)BPCL:B*"feet"* or (2h)BPCL:1*"legs,"* e.g., resting feet on the handlebars, swinging legs outward.

Examples

Sitting sideways on the crossbar

—Use sign glossed as RIDE-BIKE;

—describe crossbar using DCL;

—use SCL:V to show the person moving from the seat to the crossbar.

Riding without hands

—Use sign glossed as RIDE-BIKE;

—(no description of bike part);

—use (2h)ICL to show the person holding and then letting go of the handlebars.

Placing feet on handlebars

—Use sign glossed as RIDE-BIKE;

—describe the handlebars using DCL;

—fingerspell *"feet"* and then use (2h)BPCL:B*"feet"* to show the feet steering the handlebars.

b. **Bicycle stunt (maneuvering the bicycle)**

- Describe terrain (if not flat) using DCL, e.g., a bumpy road, big dip, curb, or obstacle.

- Describe the bicyclist holding the handlebars using (2h)ICL. Establish movement agreement between the rider and the bicycle, e.g., holding the handlebars with head and hands bouncing while going over a bumpy road, or head jerking back as you enact "pulling bicycle up" for a wheelie.

- Describe the stunt by using SCL:3 and LCL:B on your weak hand to represent the surface, e.g., flying through the air, landing with a bounce, doing a wheelie.

Examples

Doing a jump over a curb

—Describe curb using DCL;

—use (2h)ICL*"holding handlebars"* and jerk your head back as you enact "pulling up" handlebars to make bicycle jump;

—reestablish curb with LCL:B on your weak hand and use SCL:3 to show how the bicycle went over the curb.

Doing a wheelie

—(Flat terrain, no description);

—use (2h)ICL*"holding handlebars"* and jerk your head up as you enact "pulling up" handlebars to bring the front wheel up;

—use LCL:B on your weak hand to represent the ground while you use SCL:3 to show the bike traveling on the back wheel.

c. **Two people on a bicycle (shows riders' positions)**
- Establish the position of the first person steering.
  —Sign RIDE-BIKE.
- Establish the position of the "other" person.
  —Describe the bicycle part involved.
  —Use SCL:V to show the person's position.
  —Use (2h)ICL or BPCL to further describe the person's actions, e.g., holding on to the first person, legs dangling in the air

Example

Riding a bicycle with a second person sitting on the handlebars
—tell about the first person steering by using sign RIDE-BIKE;
—establish handlebars by using raised eyebrows and DCL to describe using handlebars, then use SCL:V*"person"* on (wh)LCL:1*"handlebars"* to indicate a person sitting on the handlebars

2. **Tell What Happened (see Classifier Sequence, pages 87–88, for an example)**

Review how to sequence the information and time reactions when telling what happened.

a. **Describe barrier/terrain**
- Name the barrier (curb, steps, hole, etc.)
- Then use DCL to describe size and shape of barriers.

b. **Tell how the bicycle hit the barrier/terrain (impact)**
- Indicate that what is about to happen next is unexpected (transition)
- Establish the barrier's location using LCL and then show how the bicycle (using SCL:3) hit the barrier
- Time the "pow" expression, which is a mouth snap and a eye blink, as the bicycle hits the barrier.

c. **Show how the person fell and landed**
- Reestablish the person on the bike using LCL:B for the bike and SCL:V for the person
- Show the person falling off the bike by using SCL:V. The hand used to represent the bicycle, LCL:B, is now used to represent the ground to show where the person landed. Use the "ahh" expression as the person falls through the air and "pow" expression when the person hits the ground.

"A Bicycle Incident" by Stefanie

View. Watch Stefanie describe her bicycle incident. Then go back and analyze how Stefanie addresses the narrative sequence in her story.

Rehearse. Play the video again and study how the reactions are timed to make the action sequence clear and vivid. Follow-up by rehearsing the incident until you can sign it with ease.

Below is an example of classifier sequencing for review.

Classifier Sequence. Tell what happened (bicycle hitting a curb)

establish the person riding a bicycle

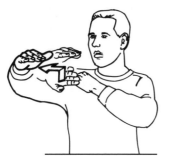

describe the barrier (DCL)

show the impact of the bike against the barrier (LCL for barrier; SCL for bike)

reestablish the rider on the bike and then show how s/he fell

establish the ground and show how the person landed

LANGUAGE NOTES

Essential Classifiers

Classifiers Used to Represent a Bicycle

When describing the movements of a bicycle, the bicycle can be represented by three classifiers:

This semantic classifier, SCL:3, is used to show a bicycle's movement and location. It is also used to describe the bicycle's spatial relationship to a person, object, or another vehicle. For example, to describe how a bike hits a person, you would use a semantic classifier to represent both the bike and the person's position and to describe how the bike hit the person.

This combination of classifiers is used when describing a person, SCL:V, straddling a bicycle, LCL:B. The only time a bicycle is represented by the "B" handshape is when you talk about the rider on the bicycle.

The following locative classifier is used to describe a spinning/turning movement. In this case, (2h)LCL:1*"spinning"* is substituted for SCL:3 to describe a bicycle spinning on one wheel.

Classifier Showing How a Rider Manipulates a Bicycle

This instrument classifier is used to show how the bicyclist holds or handles something, in this case the handlebars.

Classifiers Used to Describe Parts of the Bicycle

Bicycle parts are described from the perspective of sitting on bicycle.

handlebars

crossbar

bumper

wheel

Classifiers Used to Describe Changing Position of Rider

standing on the seat

riding with no hands

taking feet off the pedals

legs dangling out to the side

Classifiers Used to Describe Terrain

flat surface

bumpy surface

big dip in the ground

ledge

Classifiers Used to Describe Incidents Involving Barriers

Descriptive classifiers (DCL) are primarily used to describe the size and shape of barriers. An LCL classifier is used to represent the barrier when describing what happened.

Follow this structure to describe incidents involving barriers.

1. Name the barrier
2. Describe the barrier
3. Describe the accident

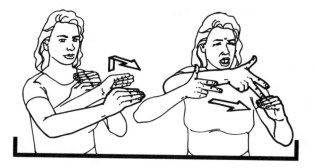

barrier: curb

barrier: tree root

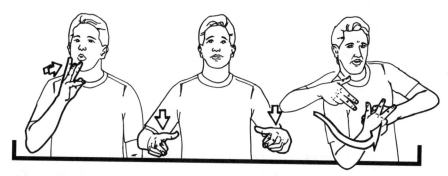

barrier: puddle

barrier: car door

Facial Expressions for Falls/Impact

Use these facial expressions when describing a bicycle incident

"aah"

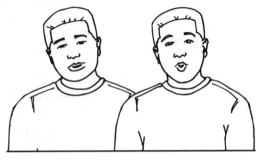

"pow"

For example: the rider on the bicycle hit a curb ("pow"), flew through the air ("ahh"), and then landed on the ground ("pow").

Others

This sign indicates that what caused the accident can't be recalled or known. See Unit 18, pages 29–30, for other transition signs.

This phrase is used when discussing hindsight. Hindsight is another way to transition into the story by telling us what should have happened before telling us what did happen. Here is the phrase to use when discussing hindsight.

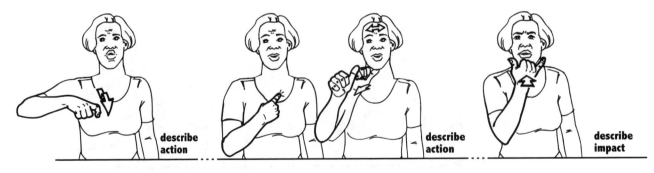

describe action   describe action   describe impact

"Terrylene's Moving Violation"

Instructions   You will examine a story about a person getting a ticket and complete the following activities. At the end of the lesson you will develop your own story about a moving violation.

Questions and Answers

View. "Terrylene's Moving Violation" and then answer the questions below.

1. Why did the policeman give Terrylene a ticket?

2. Identify the positions of Terrylene's car and the police motorcycle at the time of the violation and use dotted lines to show where the vehicles ended up.

    Below is a diagram of the scene of the traffic violation.

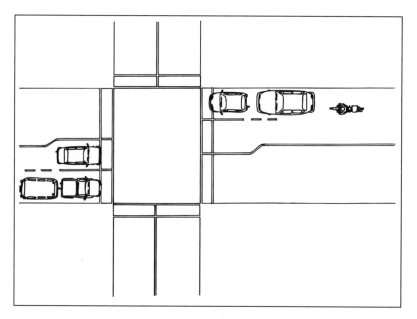

3a. Explain what happened the first time she was stuck behind the truck.

3b. What does Terrylene mean when she says she would have been better off staying behind the truck the second time?

3c. What expenses did Terrylene incur?

4. When Terrylene tried to justify her actions, what was the policeman's reaction?

5. Why did Terrylene become irritated with the policeman?

6. How do you think having Terrylene's son in the car affected how she behaved and felt?

7. Do you think Terrylene's son is deaf or hearing? Support your position with examples from the story.

Definitions

View. The narrative will be shown again. This time you are to write a definition for each of the signs listed below. To help you identify the sign, a number will appear on the screen just before the intended sign.

1.

Definition: _____

2.

Definition: _____

3.

Definition: _____

4.

Definition: _____

5.

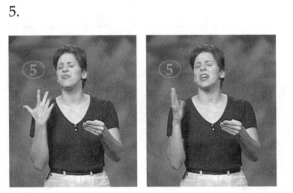

Definition: _____

6.

Definition: _____

7.

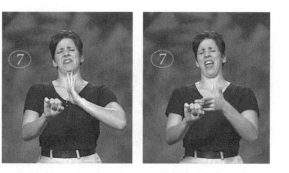

Definition: _____

8.

Definition: _____

9.

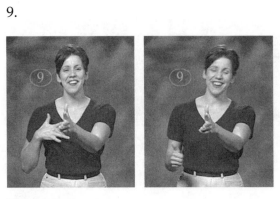

Definition: _____

10.

Definition: _____

11.

Definition: _____

12.

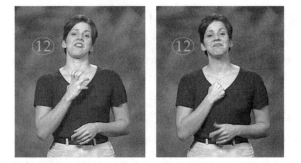

Definition: _____

Story about a Moving Violation

Prepare your own narrative about getting a moving violation ticket. It can be an incident where you were the driver or where you were a passenger. Use this narrative structure to develop your story and be prepared to tell it in class.

Narrative Structure: Getting a Ticket

I. Introduction
   a. Establish the location
   b. Specify the position of the vehicles and people involved
   c. Tell what you were thinking or doing at the time

II. Body
   a. Tell what happened
      1. your reaction when you were pulled over
      2. the conversation between you and the policeman
      3. the policeman's attitude and response
   b. Explain how it ended

III. Conclusion
   a. Offer hindsight
   b. Comment

ASSIGNMENT

"Missy's Car Accident"

Instructions: You will study a video segment about a car accident. Complete the follow-up activities and learn to retell parts of the story.

Questions and Answers

View. "Missy's Car Accident" and answer the questions below.

1. Three people were involved in the accident. Who were they and where did they sit in the car?

2. What transition sign was used to signal the beginning of the body of the story?

3. When the driver lost control of the car as it spun, what sensations did she have?

4. The car landed upside down. How did she indicate this when she described herself and the car?

5. How old was she at the time of the accident?

Facial Expressions (Clips 1–8)

View. Now, watch the following clips from "Missy's Car Accident" and circle the description that best describes the meaning of the facial expression indicated by the arrow on the screen.

Clip 1: This facial expression means Missy was _____.

  a. feeling frustrated

  b. being naive

  c. having qualms

  d. scared

Clip 2: This facial expression means Missy was driving _____.

  a. unwarily

  b. cautiously

  c. indifferently

Clip 3: This facial expression means the seat belt _____.

  a. got stuck

  b. strangled her

  c. gripped her

Clip 4: This facial expression means Missy felt _____.

  a. confused

  b. terrified

  c. agitated

Clip 5: This facial expression means the car _____.

  a. was sliding down the hill

  b. was propelled into the air

  c. rolled into the water

Clip 6: This facial expression means Missy was _____.

  a. in a state of shock

  b. gasping for air

  c. yelling for help

Clip 7: This facial expression means Missy was _____.

    a. rushing to get out

    b. injured

    c. struggling to get out

Clip 8: This facial expression means Missy was _____.

    a. angrily exiting the car

    b. straining to get out of the car

    c. calmly getting out of the car

Retell

View. Watch the following two excerpts from Missy's story and learn to retell these two segments for the next class.

Segment 1

From the time the car goes into the spin to the time it goes over an embankment and lands upside down.

Segment 2

From the time Missy looks over her situation in the car after it landed upside down to the time she managed to get out of the car and up the hill.

Tips to Learning the Story

1. Understand the segment completely.
2. Determine what part of the segment is told by the narrator and what part is told from a character's perspective.
3. Notice the pace used to tell the story and the timing of the facial expressions.
4. Rehearse the story. Try to achieve the same emotional quality.

Telling about Car Accidents

When discussing car accidents involving one or more cars, you learned this basic narrative sequence.

> **Narrative Sequence**
> 1. Describe the situation
> 2. Tell what happened
>   a. what lead up to the collision
>   b. how the car(s) collided
>   c. the damages the car(s) sustained
>   d. the injuries the people involved sustained

What follows is a discussion of what to include in each part of the narrative sequence.

1. Describe the Situation

For this part of the narrative, the information varies, but the goal remains the same: to give sufficient background to create a context for the story. Some helpful things are describing the purpose of the trip, the car (if essential to story), where people are seated in the car, and the environment or road conditions.

Recall Anthony and Missy's introductions to their accident stories. Anthony joins his neighbor in his fancy sports car to go try out a new gym. Missy describes taking her friend on her first skiing trip in her friend's Camaro.

2. Tell what happened

a. What lead up to the collision

Specify the environment, actions, or intentions that directly led up to the accident.

- **Environment.** Describe the environment if it helps explain the cause of the accident. For example, a blind spot at an intersection, a rough road, a wet or icy road, a sharp curve in the road, traffic lights, or bad weather.

- **Actions/intentions.** Explain what the driver did or intended to do just before the accident happened. In Anthony's story, he described a pager distracting the driver of the car, causing the impatient driver behind him to pull around Anthony's car, hoping to catch the green light. At the same time the driver of the car coming from the other direction was trying to beat the red light. In Missy's story, she describes how she felt worried and pulled over to ask everybody in the car to put on their seat belts before she got back on the road.

b. **How the car(s) collided.**

The moment of impact is the focal point of these stories. This is where classifiers, spatial agreement, and correct timing of facial expressions are crucial to describing the accident. Remember to establish the situation before telling what happened.

- **Spatial agreement.** For a clear description, it is important to establish and maintain spatial agreement among the cars, barriers, and people involved. If you are involved in the accident, describe the location of things and people from inside the car ("inside" perspective). If you are a bystander witnessing an accident, describe the accident as you saw it ("outside" perspective).

- **Timing of facial expressions.** As always, facial expressions including mouth movements are essential to the success of a story, e.g., describing a big crash ("pow"), small fender bender ("pop"), spinning fast, flying through the air ("ahh"), anticipating the collision ("ee"). (Review the expressions identified in Missy's car story, pages 103–104.)

- **Sensations.** Often people remember the sensation they felt during the accident—feeling as if everything is moving in slow motion, having a near death experience, or seeing surrealistic images like old silent films. In Anthony's story, he describes that witnessing the accident was like watching a silent movie where everything seems detached and unreal. In Missy's story, she describes seeing her life pass before her eyes as the car spun out of control.

c. **Describe damage to car.**

Most accidents result in some kind of damage, a small dent, a big one, or scratches. Describe the damages to the car from an "inside" perspective, whether you are involved in the accident or a bystander witnessing the accident.

d. **Injuries people involved sustained.**

Accidents often result in some kind of injury to the people involved. Injuries are usually described as part of the conclusion. Review classifiers or signs used to describe injuries on pages 26–28.

Movement Agreement

In class, you discussed two kinds of movement agreement, one between the driver and his/her car and one between the driver and the movement of the other cars. Review how these are done.

Movement Agreement between the Driver and His/Her Car

To show movement agreement you must coordinate the movements of the driver so they reflect the movement of the car. For example, a car traveling over a bumpy road is shown through the bouncing of both the driver's hands on the steering wheel and the driver's head.

Movement Agreement between the Driver and the Movement of Other Cars

To show movement agreement, you must sequence your actions and reactions with what the other cars do. For example, a driver waiting to pass the car in front of them, puts his/her head out the window to see if there's a car coming, and pulls his/her head in when the car goes by. Continuing this swaying movement of the head in and out establishes movement agreement with the cars that pass by.

Movement agreement may occur in any part of your story. Recall two scenes in Missy's story where movement agreement is used.

1. In the scene where the car goes into a spin, the driver's head moves in agreement with the spinning car.

2. Again, movement agreement is used when Missy describes an old couple approaching slowly in an old "boat" of a car.

Vocabulary Review

Road-Related Terms

street, road, lane

freeway, highway, throughway

two-lane highway

You can describe up to five lanes in each direction by using the fingers of both hands to represent the lanes in each direction.

windy country road

road on rolling hills

intersection or crossroad

stop light (use with red, yellow, or green to specify which color of light)

Telling about an Accident

The two signs below tell about an accident involving two or more vehicles. The first one depicts a collision involving minimal danger or a minor bump. The second one depicts a collision causing serious damage to one or both cars.

two-car collision

two-car collision causing serious damage

Classifiers Used to Represent Vehicles

There are two basic classifiers used to show a parked or moving car.

This semantic classifier, SCL:3, used earlier to represent a bicycle, is also used to represent vehicles, such as a car, a truck, an ambulance, or a motorcycle. This classifier can be used to indicate the vehicle's location, direction of movement, or manner of movement.

This classifier, LCL:B, applies to vehicles that are wide or flat. This classifier can be used interchangeably with the semantic classifier SCL:3 to represent many of the same vehicles—except for motorcycles.

To show the movement of two cars simultaneously use either the semantic or locative classifier for vehicles on both hands. Examples are two cars racing side by side, one car passing the other, or one car going right while the other car is going left.

Classifiers Used to Describe Two-Car Collisions

To describe collisions involving at least two cars use either the SCL:3 or SCL:B classifiers to describe exactly where the cars collided (on the side, in the front, or in the back) and to show the directions the cars traveled after the impact (to the left, to the right, forward, or sideswiping).

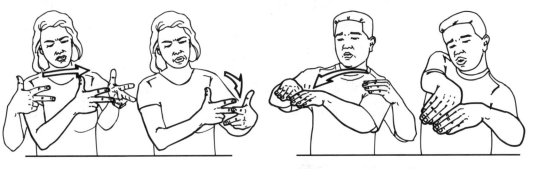

collision on rear of right side

collision on front of left side

Classifiers Used to Describe a One-Car Collision

To describe an accident involving only one car establish the surface or barrier on the weak hand and use either classifier SCL:3 or LCL:B to show how the car crashed into the barrier.

car hitting a wall

car sliding

car hitting a tree

car hitting a pole

Classifiers Used to Describe Damages to a Car

To describe common damages sustained by a car in a collision use these two basic descriptive classifiers.

Serious Damage

front

side

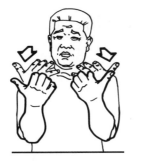

back

Small/Minor Damage

front

side

back

Scratches

This classifier describes scratches made to the side of a car as the result of a collision.

No Damage

To tell that no visible damage has occurred in a collision use the signs shown here.

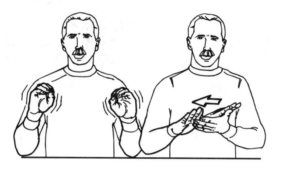

Describing Results

To say that a car is totaled and cannot be reasonably repaired, use one or all of these signs:

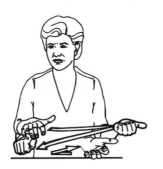

Preparing Your Narrative: Telling about an Accident

Instructions: Think of an accident that happened to you or someone you know that involves either a horse, a bicycle, or a car. Develop a story about the accident. Your story should be 3 to 5 minutes long. Follow the narrative structure below to prepare your story.

Final presentation date: _____

Narrative Structure

I. Introduction
  A. Establish the context for the story. Include one or more of these:
    1. what happened in the past
    2. the reason for the outing/situation
    3. routine or habit
    4. when it took place

II. Body
  A. Set up the scene before the accident.
    1. Describe the situation
    2. Describe the intentions of people involved
    3. Include hindsight, if helpful
  B. Describe the accident
    1. Use a conjunction to transition to describing the incident
    2. Use classifiers to describe the actions and results
    3. Vary movements to show fast/slow/out of control
    4. Use facial expressions to describe impact
    5. Use role shift to show comments, thoughts, and reactions
    6. Describe results

III. Conclusion
  A. Frame the story. Use one or more of these:
    1. what was learned (add hindsight if helpful)
    2. what happened afterward
    3. general comments about the experience itself.

To prepare your story:
- Review the video "Missy's Car Accident"
- Read review notes for Bicycle/Horse Incidents and Car Accidents on pages 73–76, 84–88, and 105–106, and Language Notes pages 77–82, 89–94, 107–115.
- Bring a VHS videotape if your teacher requests it.

TALKING ABOUT MONEY

Talking about money is inevitable—we compare prices on clothes and furniture, discuss purchases we've made, brag about bargains we've found, commiserate when we spend a fortune on car repairs, ask about borrowing and paying off debts, discuss how best to save money for the future, and so on. This unit introduces you to money-related signs so you can discuss financial topics with others.

Goal of the Unit

This is a semantics unit. Since we live in and are all part of the American economy, we naturally develop signs to match the words that are commonly used to talk about finances—words like deposit, withdrawal, loan, interest, paid off, bounced check, investment, and dividends. However, not all signs mean exactly the same as their English counterparts. You will learn when and how to use these money signs appropriately.

Buying a Car—New or Used

Instructions Understand the video dialogue in order to define money-related signs.

Questions and Answers

View. Watch the video dialogue "Buying a Car—New or Used" and answer the questions below.

1. Which car was Missy interested in buying?

   Honda Accord - 4 door

2. How much of a down payment could Missy afford?

   max 3,000

3. How long did Missy want to take to pay off the loan?

   5 years

4. Besides making a cash down payment, what was Missy thinking about doing?

   Exchanging her car

5. Summarize the pros and cons of buying a new car vs. a used car in the following areas.

   Interest: ___Higher for new car_____

   Monthly payment: ___Higher for new car_____

   Value of car: ___↓ for new car_____

   Car insurance: ___↑ for new car_____

6. When Nikki purchased a car a couple of years back, why didn't she buy a new car?

   B/c she was a student & b/c the value of the car decreases as soon as you drive away

7. Why does buying a used car seem to be a more attractive option for Missy?

   B/c of her budget & not wanting to lose car value.

Definitions

View. The dialogue will be shown again. This time you are to write a definition for each of the signs listed below. To help you identify the sign, a number will appear on the screen along with the intended sign.

Definition: _____ *down payment* _____

2.

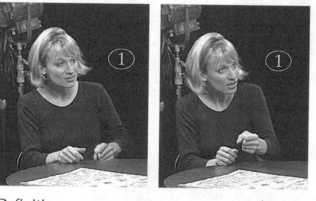

Definition: _____ *pay monthly* _____

3.

Definition: _____ pay off _____

4.

Definition: _____ interest _____

5.

Definition: _____ increase / decrease _____

6.

Definition: _____ Cost /value _____

7.

Definition: _____ Trade cars _____

8.

Definition: _____ insurance _____

9.

Definition: _____ can afford _____

10.

Definition: _____ Barely making ends meet _____

11.

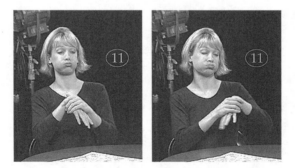

Definition: _____ Comfortable _____

Money Vocabulary

Review the money-related vocabulary discussed in class. The vocabulary is organized in categories. Review the information in a category before watching the video segments for that category. The segments show the vocabulary used in context.

Basic Money Signs

Segment 1

to pay by credit card

The words "check" and "cash" are fingerspelled.

Segment 2

to pay for someone's meal or entertainment; if the sign is two-handed, it means everyone chips in to split the bill equally

to pay for services such as a haircut or goods such as a book

Segment 3

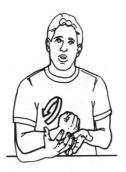

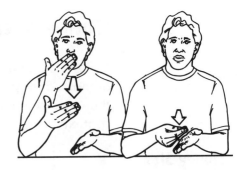

to receive money for work you have done; in another context it can mean to collect money

earning a good income

to receive money regularly from sources other than employment, e.g., pension, unemployment benefits, social security, welfare, dividends, allowances; in another context it means to subscribe to

to receive a substantial amount of money in one lump sum, e.g., an inheritance, a grant, or lottery winnings

Segment 4

to be given a gift or awarded something significant like grant money, a new car, or a scholarship

to invest in stocks

Banking Terms

Segment 5

savings; to save money; in another context it can mean to keep food or things for later, hold on to; store, set aside, or put away

The words "checking" and "account" are fingerspelled.

Segment 6

to put money in an account; to make a deposit; to put money down

to put money in a savings account only

The word "paycheck" is fingerspelled.

Segment 7

to subtract; to deduct from

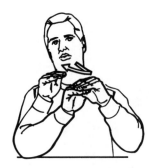

to use the automated teller machine (ATM) to get cash

The abbreviation "ATM" (automated teller machine) is fingerspelled.

insufficient funds in an account

check that is returned by the bank due to insufficient funds; a rubber check;
a check that bounced

Segment 8

interest; APR (annual percentage rate)

to transfer funds from one account/bank to another; in another context this sign can mean to transfer jobs, schools, etc.

Segment 9

to reconcile your checkbook balance with the balance on your bank statement

The words "statement" and "checkbook" are fingerspelled.

Discussing Finances

Segment 10

to make a donation to someone or to a charity

to be out of money; to be short of money; to be broke

to spend more than you really should; in another context this sign can mean to spend money recklessly

to owe someone; to be in debt; to afford to be in debt

to barely make ends meet; to live from paycheck to paycheck

The word "bills" is fingerspelled.

Segment 11

to pay for an expensive item with a large sum of cash; if the sign is repeated, it means to increase monthly payments substantially to pay off a debt sooner

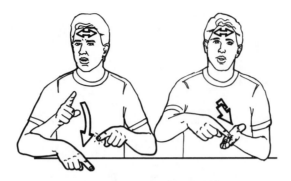

to be unable to afford something; to not have sufficient funds to make a purchase, to be unable to assume any more debts

to make monthly payments, i.e., bills, rent; to provide financial support on a regular basis, e.g., alimony, or allowances

to increase; to appreciate in value or debt

to make a purchase using a layaway plan; to pay on the unpaid balance until it is paid in full before taking the merchandise

to keep paying

to have a debt paid in full; to pay off a debt

Segment 12

to run out of money/funds; to be broke; to have zero balance in an account

to spend or pay more than you'd like or expect for something, e.g., major repairs, renovations, tuition, hospital bills, or weddings.

Segment 13

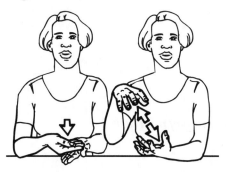

to be wealthy; to have an abundance of money

to bequeath; to present a large monetary gift to someone

to spend all of the money you have in a short period of time; to blow money

to donate to a number of causes or to people; this sign is a variation of an earlier sign shown in Segment 10, pages 128–129

to make a great deal of money from an investment, inheritance, or from gambling; a windfall

to buy; to purchase

money dwindles down until there is nothing left

to pay for everyone's expenses; to treat everybody to something

under the table; to gain favor from someone by giving him/her money; to bribe (usually refers to activity that is not aboveboard)

to get into debt; to lose money in a business venture

Segment 14

everyone contributing or pooling money

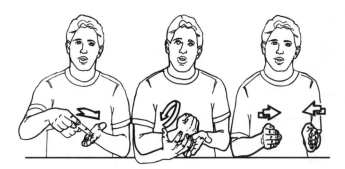

small or limited earnings

to be a cheapskate; to be stingy

to deduct from, to garnish wages, to subtract

rising cost of living

struggling to make ends meet; hardly maintaining a respectable standard of living; needy

MAKING MAJOR DECISIONS

Life is full of decisions that range from as simple as what to eat at a restaurant to as complex as where to live. For major decisions people make lists of pros and cons, gather information, and solicit the opinions of experts or of family and friends. Making major decisions is a process. Everyone can describe what they went through to make a decision like choosing a college or a career, moving to another city or state, getting married, getting a divorce, having a baby, buying a car, finding an apartment, or buying a house.

Goal of the Unit

This unit is to help you expand your vocabulary and develop conversational fluency by encouraging you to discuss your experiences. You will develop skills enabling you to talk about the choices you had at the beginning, the criteria you used to evaluate options, what you chose, and how you felt about the decisions you made. Then you will use those same skills to retell information told to you by your partner in class. You will rehearse conversation skills such as asking for clarification, elaborating, and sharing opinions.

"Deciding to Marry"

Instructions   After answering the questions below, view the video segment again to see how the signer addresses the narrative structure on page 139.

Questions and Answers

View. Watch "Deciding to Marry." Write your answers to the questions listed below.

1. Explain Missy's situation.

2. What was the issue for Missy?

3. What experiences did Missy draw upon to make her decision?

4. What did she decide? How did she arrive at her decision?

5. How does she feel about it now?

Preparing Your Narrative: Telling about a Major Decision

Instructions Prepare to sign a narrative about a major life decision you have made. It might be about choosing a college, changing careers, choosing to end a relationship, relocating to a new city, having a baby, coping with a major illness or a death in the family, or making a major investment. Use the guide below to help you think through your story. You may need specific signs to discuss your topic. If the signs you need have not been covered in class, ask around or think of a way to express the same idea using the vocabulary you know.

Narrative Structure

1. Explain the situation.
2. Explain the problems/issues.
3. Tell what experiences/information you drew on to plan the next step.
4. Tell how you arrived at your decision.
5. Tell how you feel about your decision now.

Preparing Your Narrative

Describing the Process. When discussing your process for making a decision, not all events or steps are equally important so you need to incorporate language that allows you to "fast forward" your story to significant events and yet give your listener a sense of what happened in the interim. Here are language tools you might find helpful.

Distributional Aspect Inflection. The decision-making process usually involves evaluating the various options available to us. The distributional aspect is often added to the verb sign to show that a number of people, places, or things were considered in making your decision without detailing what was said or being specific about what transpired. For example, the verb signs listed have been modified to show distributional aspect and video Clips 1 and 2 provide demonstrations in context. Read the information about each clip before watching the clip.

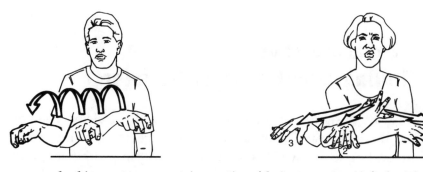

checking out or comparing options/choices   *not satisfied with the options/choices*

Clip 1

View. In this excerpt from Ken's video story, "Looking for a House," he uses the two signs illustrated above to indicate that he had checked many houses and did not like what he had seen until he came upon a house he really liked. Note the repetition of the signs move in an "arc" in front of his body to indicate he checked out a number of different houses.

Clip 2

View. In this excerpt from Byron's video story, "Buying a Car," he uses the first sign illustrated above to show he had visited a number of different car dealers before he narrowed his options to a Nissan or a Toyota.

Continuous Aspect Inflection. Another way to "fast forward" the narrative is to show yourself considering an option without being specific about what you thought about. In that case, you would inflect the verb sign to show a continuous aspect, e.g., "thinking about something for a while," or "taking the time to look something over." The verb signs here have been modified to show a continuous aspect.

The signs shown mean that someone is taking the time to think something over before coming to a final decision.

This sign refers to looking over, examining, or appraising an option.

This sign indicates searching for something s/he really wants.

This sign refers to consulting with or discussing with a person for some time before making a decision.

This sign means to waver or vacillate before making a decision.

Transition signs. After considering your options, you've reached a decision. To signal that what is to follow is your decision, these signs may be useful transitional signs.

to decide, to make up one's mind

give up, reject, or put aside an option

These signs usually follow the signs above.

move forward, go ahead, proceed

let go of, not follow through, drop the idea or plan

Ways to conclude a narrative. Conclude the narrative by telling what you think of the decision now that some time has elapsed. To show time has elapsed use one of the signs listed below. View Clips 3, 4, and 5 to see the signs used in context. Read the information about each clip before watching the clip.

since then

sometime later, later on

Clip 3

View. In this excerpt from Byron's video story, "Buying a Car," Byron uses the first sign "since then" to tell how he felt about his car.

Clip 4

View. In this excerpt from Ken's video story, "Looking for a House," Ken uses the second sign "sometime later" to explain that as time went by, and the family grew, the house was no longer adequate.

Clip 5

View. In this excerpt from Missy's story, "Deciding to Marry," she concluded her narrative using the first sign "since then".

Other Useful Vocabulary

Tell What Is Essential

Use this sign to signal that the things you are about to list or describe are essential features that you are looking for in making a decision. View Clips 6 and 7 to see the sign used in context. Read the information about each clip before watching the clip.

Clip 6

View. In this excerpt from Byron's video story, "Buying a Car," Byron uses the sign above to tell us what features are important to him when selecting a car, before listing them on his weak hand.

Clip 7

View. In this excerpt from Missy's video story, "Deciding to Marry," Missy uses this sign to begin explaining what she considers important in a relationship.

Use this sign to point out the primary reason for the action taken or for the decision made. View Clips 8, 9, and 10 to see the sign used in context. Read the information about the clips before watching them.

Clips 8, 9, and 10

View. These excerpts from Ken's video story, "Looking for a House," show Ken specifying the primary reasons for his decisions. In Clip 8, Ken's primary reason for buying a house is that it is a good investment. In Clip 9, Ken's primary reason for searching in one specific location is because he wanted to live in the city of Riverside. In Clip 10, Ken's primary reason for buying an older home is that it's less expensive.

Tell What You Don't Want to Be Bothered with

This sign refers to not wanting to be bothered with doing something, or not wanting to have anything to do with something. In discussing the process of reaching a major decision, you may use this sign to explain why you rejected an option. View Clips 11, 12, and 13 to see the sign used in context. Read the information about each clip before watching the clip.

Clip 11

View. This excerpt from Ken's video story shows him talking about the drawbacks of a two-story house. Ken uses the sign to show what he doesn't want to be bothered with—going up and down stairs.

Clip 12

View. In this excerpt from Byron's video story he uses the sign to talk about why he wants an automatic transmission rather than a manual one.

Clip 13

View. This excerpt from Missy's video story shows her using this sign to express her initial concern about getting into a serious relationship in case she wanted to change her situation, move, or see someone else.

Vocabulary Review

Discussing Housing   You may find this vocabulary useful when discussing housing.

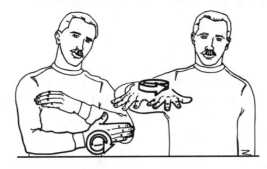

in the countryside, rural

having a nice view

peaceful, quiet

wonderful, neat, swell

landlord, landlady

neighborhood

roomy or a comfortable size

extremely large or huge

Comments about Lack of

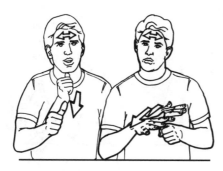

not having enough of

to make the best of what little you have

Comments about Cost/Rent

inexpensive, cheap

reasonable, average for that area

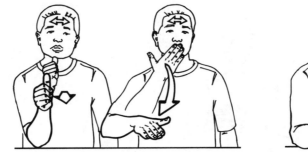

not bad, within range

expensive

Discussing Cars   You may find this vocabulary useful when discussing cars.

Parts of a Car

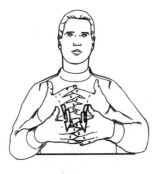

engine

clutch

transmission

cylinders

stick shift

automatic (transmission)

The words "tires" and "brakes" are fingerspelled. "Air conditioning" is spelled AC.

Problems with Cars

bald or bare tires

guzzles gas; uses up a lot of gas

engine repeatedly stalls

car breaks down

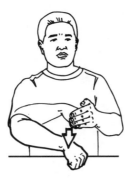

blow the engine

Others

powerful

test drive

includes everything

Talking about Car Problems

Use this sign to describe something whose quality is so bad or defective that it can be dangerous to use or operate, e.g., brakes that are so seriously defective it is unsafe to drive the car, tires that are so bald it's unsafe to drive.

Use this sign to refer to something that doesn't work well or is of poor quality.

Use this sign to refer to something that has caused problems repeatedly, requiring you to send the car to the shop for repairs often, e.g., windshield wipers not working right, problems with the brakes.

Discussing Life Changes

Choosing a College

program

major

training

support

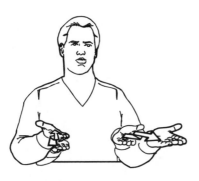

service

diversity/variety

The word "scholarship" is fingerspelled.

Talk about Reputation

wonderful, excellent   *well-known, famous*

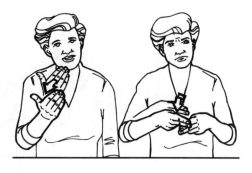

reputable

DISCUSSING HEALTH CONDITIONS

In everyday conversations you may find yourselves in situations where you need to explain complex ideas in ASL. This unit on health introduces you to language skills that will help you organize and discuss complex topics.

Goal of the Unit

This unit will prepare you to take complex information written on a particular illness, identify the important points to cover, organize the information into three areas, symptoms, causes, and treatments, and make a concise 5-minute presentation.

ASSIGNMENT

"How One Breathes"

Instructions   You will analyze the presentation about the respiratory process and practice retelling the information.

Questions and Answers

View. Watch "How One Breathes," by Marlon Kuntze. Answer the questions below.

1. For which parts of the breathing process did Marlon use role shift?

2. How does the respiratory system work? List the process Marlon described.

3. What analogy did Marlon use for the lungs? Why do you think it was used?

4. How did Marlon begin and end his presentation?
   Begin:

   End:

5. How did Marlon handle the following terminology?

"breathe"—

"oxygen"—

"carbon dioxide"—

"air sacs"—

"capillary"—

Rehearse. Rehearse explaining the process of breathing you listed in question 2. Rehearse this portion until you are comfortable describing the process. Incorporate role shift and classifiers in your retelling.

CLASSROOM

Exercise 1: Learning the Parts

Instructions   Study the four diagrams and become familiar with the parts and their relationship to each other. Read the information to learn how the eye, ear, digestive system, and reproductive system work. Be prepared to describe their normal processes.

The Eye

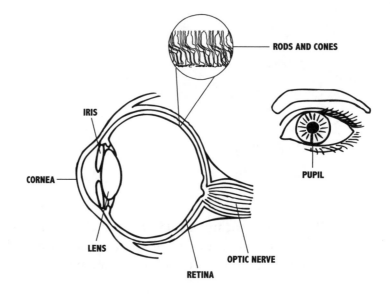

- The amount of light allowed to enter the eye is regulated by the **pupil.** The diameter of the pupil is controlled by the expansion and contraction of muscles in the **iris.** When the room becomes bright, the pupil constricts and when the room becomes dark the pupil expands. As the eyes adapt to the new level of light, the pupil returns to its original size.
- Light rays that enter the eye are focused by the **cornea** and **lens** and an inverted image is then projected on the retina which is at the back of the eye.
- When an object is viewed from a distance, the lens is fairly flat. As the object moves nearer, the lens increasingly thickens or curves outward until the image is no longer blurred.
- The **retina** is made of several layers of nerve cells and one layer of **rods** and **cones.** Light strikes the rods and cones and then passes back to the nerve cells in order to generate nerve impulses. The rods are sensitive to dim light and are important in black-white vision and the detection of motion. Cones are responsible for color vision and for the perception of bright images.
- The nerve impulses are channeled through the **optic nerve,** which relays the information to the **visual cortex** at the rear of the brain, which then interprets the data it receives.

The Ear

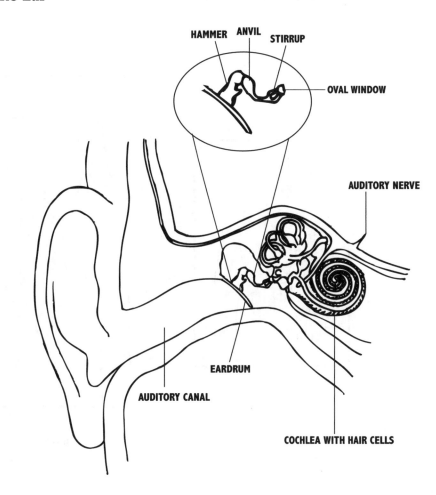

- Sounds first enter the outer ear by traveling down the **auditory canal** and then causing the **eardrum** to vibrate.
- The vibrations are then transmitted through the middle ear by a sequence of three tiny bones called the **hammer, anvil,** and **stirrup.**
- The last of the bones, the stirrup, rests on a membrane (the **oval window**) in the bony wall of the **cochlea** (the inner ear) and carries the vibrations to fluids, creating waves on a membrane running along the length of the cochlea.
- On the membrane are thousands of **hair cells** which serve as sound receptors. When sound waves hit them, they send electrical impulses through the **auditory nerve** to the brain. Nerve impulses from each region along the membrane are relayed to different regions of the brain, and what you hear—high, low, loud, soft sounds—depends on which area of the brain is stimulated.

The Digestive System

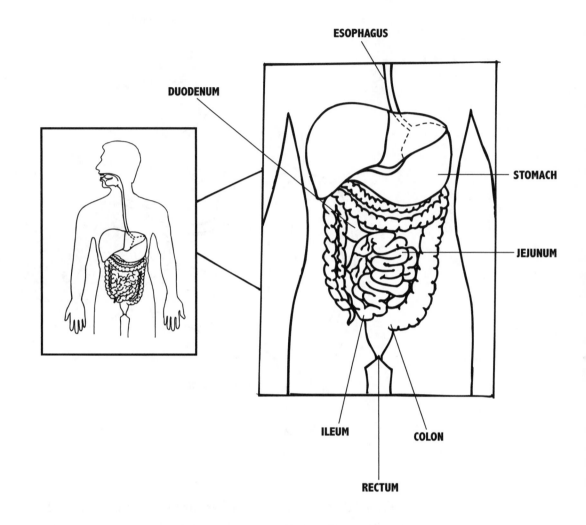

- Food first enters the mouth, where it is chewed into smaller pieces—enzymes in the saliva are released to begin breaking down the food's sugars and to help make chewing and swallowing easier.
- Food then passes through the **esophagus** into the **stomach,** where it is liquefied by a mixture of acid and pepsin.
- The contents of the stomach go down into the **duodenum** (the first portion of the small intestine)—a duct from the pancreas and the gall bladder into the duodenum secretes enzymes for further breakdown of proteins and carbohydrates.
- The food mass now passes through **jejunum** (the next portion of the small intestine) where the bulk of the digested food is absorbed into the body.
- The remaining nutrients move on to the **ileum** (the last third of the small intestine) where fat, fat-soluble vitamins, vitamin B-12, and bile salts are absorbed.
- Indigestible residues are passed through into the **colon.** Here additional water is extracted.
- Finally, the residues are passed into the **rectum** for evacuation.

The Reproductive System

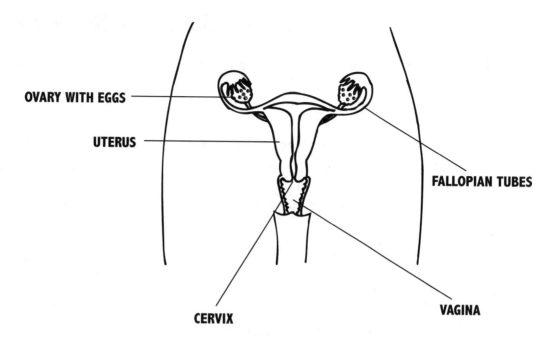

OVARY WITH EGGS

UTERUS

FALLOPIAN TUBES

CERVIX

VAGINA

- The **ovaries** are connected to the **uterus** by **Fallopian tubes.**
- During ovulation, the lining of the uterus thickens in preparation to receive and nourish a fertilized egg.
- Once every month the ovaries release an **egg.**
- For fertilization to occur, the sperm must reach the egg within 24 hours of its release from the ovary. Once fertilized, the egg takes about 3 days to make the short journey from ovary to uterus to become implanted.
- **First trimester**—the fetus develops a simple brain and eyes. The heart begins to beat. The ears, nose, mouth, fingers, and toes are easily recognizable, and the sex of the baby is clear.
- **Second trimester**—the thin-walled skin develops, organs begin to function, and blood begins to be formed in the bone marrow. Scalp hair appears and bones begin to harden. The fetus begins to move.
- **Third trimester**—The majority of the baby's weight is gained during this time. Ear lobes begin to develop cartilage, testes begin to descend into the scrotum, nails begin to grow over the tips of the fingers and toes. The fetus begins to behave with cycles of wakefulness and activity similar to that of a newborn.
- During birth, the **cervix,** a passageway between the uterus and **vagina,** widens and the muscles of the uterus (womb) contract pushing the baby out along the passageway into the world.

Exercise 2: Explaining the Normal Process

Instructions   You are to develop a presentation describing the normal process of one of the four topics: eye, ear, digestive system, or reproductive system.

Follow these steps to develop your presentation.

Step 1—Introduce the Topic by Using a Rhetorical Question

A rhetorical question is an effective way to direct the listener's attention to the topic of the presentation. In Marlon's presentation, he begins with the rhetorical question "What are we going to discuss now? He responds with "Breathing!"

Step 2—Tell How the Process Begins

Identify what activates the process. For example, Marlon begins with how a breath is taken in.

Step 3—Explain the Process

- *Use classifiers* to describe each body part involved.
  a. Begin by pointing to where the body part is located on your body.
  b. Describe its shape, behavior, and function in neutral space.
      For example, Marlon points out where the lungs are located on the body and then describes how the lungs function, in particular the air sacs. In neutral space, Marlon shows how oxygen passes through the air sacs to the blood.

- *Use role shift* to show how the parts behave in relation to each other.
      For example, Marlon role shifts to show how the capillary and the blood exchange oxygen and CO_2. Using an analogy may help the audience visualize how a system or its parts work. Recall how Marlon used a tree analogy to create a visualization of part of the lungs.

- *Use raised eyebrows* to signal the introduction of the next topic or when referring to a previous topic.
      For example, after Marlon mentions that what goes out of the mouth is called CO_2 he spells CO_2. He raises his eyebrows while spelling "C" with his weak hand and pointing to that hand. He then spells out "carbon" to indicate what the letter "C" refers to. He does the same for O_2.
      Raised eyebrows are also used with rhetorical questions to signal that what follows is an explanation of the next part of the process. For example, Marlon uses a rhetorical question to ask the name of something he has just described (capillary). He then goes on to describe the function of capillaries.

Step 4—Tell How the Process Ends

Marlon ends the description of the breathing process by describing exhaling (air goes out of mouth).

Step 5—Close with a Comment

Marlon closes his presentation by commenting that the breathing process happens every minute of every day and that it's quite amazing!

Exercise 3: Migraine

Instructions Read over the cards. Practice explaining symptoms, causes, and treatments.

Signer A—patient

Symptoms: Throbbing pain on one side of the head or all over the head, feeling nauseous, eyes becoming more sensitive to bright lights, eyesight becoming blurry

---

Signer B—health care expert

Possible condition: Migraine

Causes: No one *really* knows what causes migraine. Headaches can be made worse from food allergy, birth control pill, not enough sleep, tension, and menstrual cycle.

Treatment: Aspirin sometimes helps for an existing migraine and can also be taken daily to reduce migraine frequency. If aspirin is not effective, prescriptions are available for painkillers or drugs that are designed to constrict the blood vessels surrounding the brain. Patients should cut down on eating certain foods that cause blood vessels to dilate such as chocolate, aged cheese, liver, eggplant, and alcohol.

Signer C—health care expert

Possible condition: Migraine

Causes: No one *really* knows what causes migraine. Headaches can be made worse from food allergy, birth control pill, not enough sleep, tension, and menstrual cycle.

Treatment: Massage areas around the head, spine, eyes, and sinuses. Exercise regularly. Avoid caffeine, alcohol, red meat, food preservatives, MSG, and processed meats. Use hot and cold water compresses alternately on the head.

Describing Symptoms, Causes, and Treatments

Instructions To explain the symptoms, causes, and treatments for a health condition, use the following sequence to structure the information.

> **Discuss a condition**
> 1. Name the condition and briefly describe the symptoms.
> 2. Describe the causes.
> 3. Discuss treatment options.
>   a. Tell if it is curable.
>   b. List treatment options on your weak hand.

Example: Migraine

1. Name the condition and briefly describe the symptoms

- To begin, fingerspell the word "migraine" and then give a description of common symptoms associated with a migraine.

2. Describe the causes

- To transition to discussing causes, use the rhetorical question illustrated below.

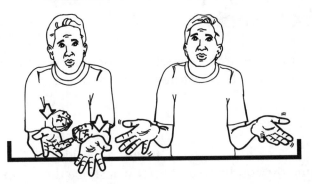

- List the causes on your weak hand.
- Use raised eyebrows each time you refer to a finger on your weak hand to signal that you are naming the next cause.
- Since causes are often written as noun phrases, you must translate the phrases into action verbs. The following are examples of probable causes for migraines. Study how the noun phrases are translated.

for "birth control pills"

for "food allergies"

for "menstruation cycles"

3. Discuss treatment options

- To transition to discussing treatment options, use a rhetorical question with the appropriate phrase to tell whether or not a condition is curable.

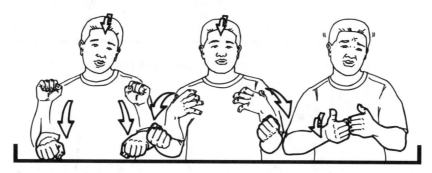

can recover completely

symptoms can be eliminated

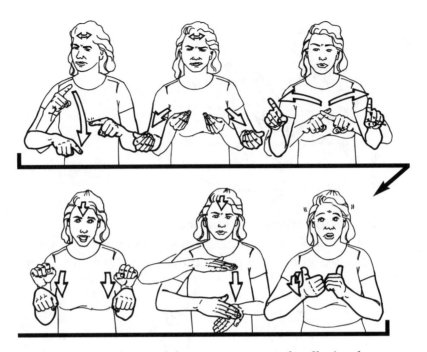

condition cannot be cured, but symptoms can be alleviated

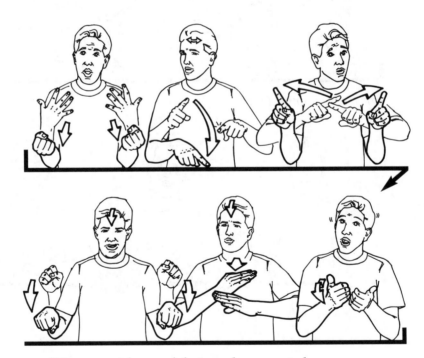

condition cannot be cured, but can be prevented

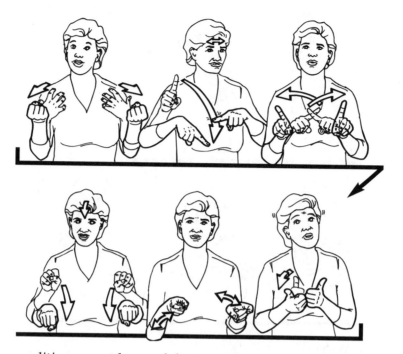

condition cannot be cured, but symptoms can be controlled

- Like with causes, use raised eyebrows each time you refer to a finger on your weak hand before describing a treatment option.
- Ways of handling medication terminology.
    1. If the type of medicine has a standard sign, use it.
    2. If the medication terminology is common and there's no sign for it, fingerspell it out. You would spell "aspirin," "peroxide," and "Ben Gay." Follow with a description of its purpose like "to reduce headache," "to prevent infection," or "to provide relief."
    3. If the medication terminology is not common, you don't need to fingerspell the word, just describe how it is taken (pills, shots, nosespray) and for what purpose. Take the word "corticosteroids"— explain that it is taken as a pill and that its purpose is to provide relief from pain (see next page).

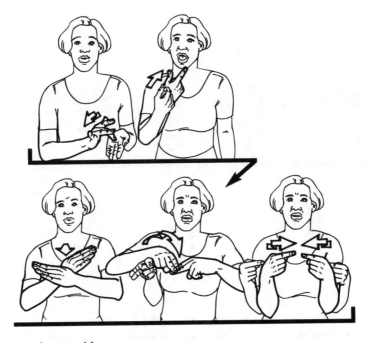

corticosteroids

Definitions

This sign is used when referring to the person's recovery from an illness that affected the whole body like cancer or from being bedridden and then being able to get up.

This sign is used when referring to the eventual disappearance of symptoms such as sores, rashes, lumps, fevers, or headaches.

In this case, this sign means to lessen the pain or symptoms associated with the condition.

This sign means to maintain a constant level where fluctuations are common, e.g., blood sugar, blood pressure, or weight.

This sign refers to actions taken to prevent damage to the body, or to prevent the body from succumbing to an illness.

Translations   Review the vocabulary used to discuss treatment options and their appropriate translations.

Treatment Options

Apply

For phrases containing the word "apply," such as to "apply pressure," "apply ointment," and "apply powder," use a BCL or an ICL and show how it is applied.

apply ointment

apply pressure to the point located at the base of the little toe...

Take

For phrases containing the word "take," use the following translations.

take vitamins or pills

take a shower

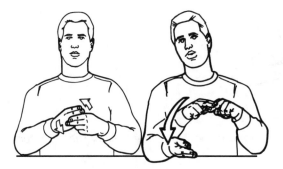

take some weight off

Use

For phrases referring to medications and containing the word "use" such as "use nasal spray" or "use topical cream," use an ICL to show how you take the substance.

use nasal spray

When referring to objects like "use a cane"or "use a compress," name or describe the object first and then use an ICL to show yourself using the object.

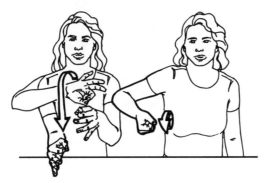

use cane

Another way is to use the sign shown below followed by a sign naming the object (noun sign).

to use (an object)

Get

For phrases containing the word "get," use the following translations.

Follow the phrase below with the fingerspelled name for a medicine like aspirin or painkiller, or give a brief description of how the medicine is taken and its purpose.

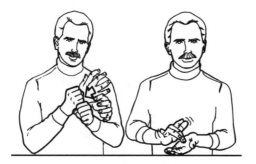

get a prescription

get an injection or vaccination

The sign below is also used for the phrase "to rid the body of toxins."

get rid of dust, mold, and mildew

Avoid

For phrases containing the word "avoid," use the following translations.

This is a general sign cautioning people to avoid something or to not do or eat something. You need to describe the action and then use this sign.

don't do it, don't take it, avoid

This sign means to physically stay away from certain things, such as pets.

stay away from, avoid

This sign means to eliminate certain things from your diet, such as red meat or alcohol.

eliminate, reject, avoid

Massage

For phrases containing the word "massage," use a BCL and show yourself massaging the specified location.

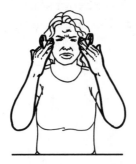

massage the area around the eyes

Soak

For phrases containing the English words "soak (parts of body) in water" use the following phrases.

soak your feet in a bowl of water

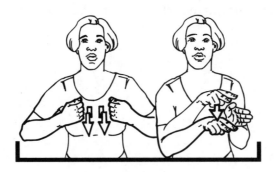

soak your body in a warm bath

Purpose of Treatments

to help, assist

to provide relief from, to reduce, to relieve symptoms

to prevent development, to prevent infection

to fight the virus

to fight the virus, eliminate the virus

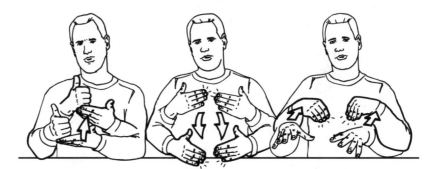

to increase tolerance

to increase flexibility

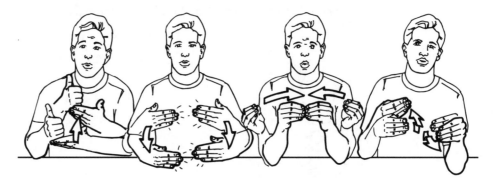

to increase mobility

Parkinson's Disease

Instructions By answering the questions below, you will examine how Nikki organized and presented the information.

Questions and Answers

View. "Parkinson's Disease" by Nikki Schmitz and answer the questions below.

Introduction

1. Parkinson's disease is described as what? What is it related to?

2. List the types of body movement mentioned.

3. Describe the symptoms associated with Parkinson's disease.

Body

1. Describe the process the brain goes through when one wants to move his/her body.

2. Describe how the process in the brain is affected by Parkinson's disease.

3. Is there a cure?

4. What kind of treatment is available? How does the medication work?

Conclusion

1. What two things are the doctors still researching regarding Parkinson's disease?

Language Features

1. How did Nikki handle this terminology?
   "Parkinson's disease"—

   "Movement"—

   "Chemical"—

   "Dopamine"—

   "L-Dopa"—

2. When did Nikki use role shift?

3. What transitions did Nikki use to begin each segment in her presentation?

4. What sign did Nikki use to end each segment in her presentation?

5. Several times throughout the presentation Nikki establishes the subject on her dominant (left) hand then points to it with her weak (right) hand. What is the function of this technique?

Diabetes

Instructions For this assignment you are to develop a draft presentation on Diabetes for class. To help you prepare your draft, read the article on Diabetes, answer the follow up questions, then use your answers to help prepare your presentation.

Diabetes mellitus

Diabetes mellitus, often called sugar diabetes, is a condition in which the body is unable to properly process carbohydrates (sugars and starches), which are the body's major source of energy.

Cause

Normally, digestion causes carbohydrates to release a form of sugar called glucose into the blood. As the blood glucose level rises, the pancreas is stimulated to secrete the hormone insulin. Insulin acts to reduce the sugar content in the blood by transporting glucose from the blood to body cells, where it is used for fuel, or to the liver, where it is stored until needed for fuel.

When the pancreas produces insufficient insulin or the body cannot use the insulin it manufactures, diabetes results. The glucose concentration in the blood increases because glucose circulates throughout the body without being absorbed. Eventually, the kidneys filter glucose from the blood, and urine carries the excess sugar from the body.

Types

There are two major forms of diabetes. Type I (or Insulin-dependent) diabetes results from a defect of unknown origin in the islets of Langer-hans (the areas in the pancreas where insulin is produced). This form of diabetes can develop in young children.

With Type II (or non-insulin-dependent) diabetes, either the pancreas functions inadequately or the body is unable to use insulin efficiently. Sometimes, a shortage of insulin-receptor cells (sites throughout the body where the interaction of glucose and insulin occurs) allows the insulin to be present in the bloodstream without working properly. Obesity often contributes to the problem because the presence of excess fat cells leads to increased resistance to insulin. Type II diabetes, which appears most often in adults over the age of 40, may evolve from a gradual slowing of insulin production within the pancreas. In addition, other disorders of the endocrine system may cause hormonal imbalances that disturb glucose regulation.

Research shows that people who have a family history of Type II diabetes may have a greater tendency to acquire the condition. Women are more likely to be affected, but for all adults, the risk of developing Type II diabetes doubles with every decade after the age of 40.

In some women, pregnancy triggers diabetes. The condition usually subsides after childbirth. However, women who show signs of diabetes during pregnancy and deliver babies weighing over ten pounds have a greater risk of diabetes later in life.

Complications

Although patients with diabetes can usually control the condition, untreated diabetes can lead to serious complications. Extremely high blood sugar levels place great strain on other organs. Diabetes may accelerate atherosclerosis (clogging of the arteries). Insufficient blood supply contributes to heart attack, stroke, kidney disease, eye disorders, impotence, gangrene (death of tissue due to inadequate blood circulation), and even death.

Symptoms

Symptoms of Type I diabetes are excessive thirst and urination, fatigue, altered vision, fainting, irritability, and slow healing of cuts and bruises. Weight loss may occur despite constant hunger and voracious eating.

The same symptoms may signal Type II diabetes, or no symptoms may appear at all. Physicians frequently detect this form when they perform routine examinations or tests for other problems.

Diagnosis

Doctors can diagnose diabetes by analyzing blood samples for elevated sugar concentrations. They may also test blood and urine for excess ketones, the chemical by-products of the breakdown of fat for energy. Since people with diabetes do not use glucose normally, their bodies burn fat for fuel, and as a result, ketones are eliminated in the urine.

Treatment

Both forms of diabetes mellitus require a treatment plan that maintains normal, steady blood glucose levels. Once blood sugar levels have been brought under control with insulin injections, diet, or medication, a person with diabetes can usually lead a nearly normal life.

Type I diabetes requires injections of insulin to maintain blood sugar levels evenly all day. If the blood glucose concentration rises, imbalance may be signalled by weakness, fatigue, and thirst. These symptoms mean that more insulin is needed. However, if blood glucose concentration falls too low, an insulin reaction sets in, causing dizziness, hunger, fatigue, headache, sweating, trembling, and (in severe cases) unconsciousness. A quick remedy for this problem is to give the person simple sugar, such as is found in orange juice and some kinds of candy. This should be done only if the person is conscious and alert, however; nothing should be given by mouth to an unconscious or semiconscious person, because of the risk of choking.

Ideally, a doctor can prevent these fluctuations of sugar levels by coordinating the type and timing of insulin injections with meal content and energy output. A special diet is important to balance daily insulin injections. Young children with diabetes, in particular, need sufficient calories to grow and develop normally. Insulin requirements for persons with Type I diabetes differ greatly. Some patients may maintain balanced blood sugar levels with one insulin injection taken before breakfast. Other patients may require several insulin injections per day. Insulin requirements may change as the patient grows older, undergoes surgery, becomes pregnant, or develops an unrelated illness.

Many people with Type II diabetes can regulate their condition with proper diet. Sometimes, oral antidiabetic drugs, which work by stimulating the pancreas to produce more insulin and/or stimulating insulin receptors, may be prescribed.

Special attention to diet is critical for diabetes control. Overweight individuals need to lose weight. Thereafter, emphasis is on eating balanced meals that will sustain the recommended weight. Fats need to be limited to reduce susceptibility to aterosclerosis, and the diet should be low in simple sugars. The diet should include plenty of fibrous roughage, such as is contained in fruits, vegetables, and whole grains; fiber in the diet has been shown to reduce or slow sugar absorption in the digestive tract.

A doctor can provide a medically approved diet plan, with enough flexibility to allow the diabetic patient to share in regular family meals while meeting his or her special dietary needs.

With either type of diabetes, follow-up is important to plan diet, determine changes in insulin dosage (in Type I), and monitor blood for sugar levels. Testing urine for sugar has been shown to be inaccurate, and the availability of home blood glucose monitoring has all but replaced urine sugar testing for most diabetic patients. Urine ketone testing, however, is still important. It has been shown in recent years that meticulous control of blood glucose levels can delay or prevent many of the complications of diabetes mellitus. Therefore, strict adherence to the regimen prescribed by the physician is of major importance.

Questions and Answers

1. What terminology is needed to discuss diabetes?

2. What are the symptoms?

3. What is the normal digestive process?

4. How is the process affected by diabetes?

5. What are the causes?

6. Is diabetes curable?

7. What kind of treatment is available?

8. If not treated, what will happen?

Prepare Your Presentation

Read the section on "Giving a Coherent Presentation" pages 189–193, and use the answers above to organize your presentation.

GUIDELINES

Preparing Your Health Presentation

Instructions Your project is to prepare a 5-minute presentation on the health condition you have chosen.

Your Topic: _____

Date of Presentation: _____

Researching
- Your teacher may give you an article on your topic. You should not rely on that article only. You should find other sources at the library or on the Internet to help you understand your topic and to get additional information.
- Your goal is to explain the condition in "everyday terms." You will present information as a lay person, not as a medical professional. Your presentation should give people *general* information about the condition. Your presentation should teach something interesting and useful.

Planning Use the following guide to plan your presentation.
- Decide what terminology is needed to discuss the condition and how you will refer to those terms throughout your presentation.
- Find out if there is an actual sign for the terminology. If the sign is not familiar to your audience, plan to write the corresponding English terminology on the board and then show the sign. If there is no sign for the word, plan to spell it out, abbreviate the word, or invent a temporary sign. (The temporary sign should not conflict with existing signs that mean something else. For example, after spelling the word "insulin," you cannot use the sign I-shake because I-shake means "infection," so you would either fingerspell it at all times or come up with a sign that won't cause confusion.)
- If you are discussing a specific organ in the body, e.g., the pancreas, plan to point to part of body where the pancreas is located.
- Pare down the information to its most basic elements. Elaborate only to clarify the most basic facts. Avoid medical terms, rare cases, or detailed information.
- Write an outline or notes to help you remember the order of the information. Do not write too many details, otherwise you might be tempted to look at your notes throughout your presentation. The outline should be written large enough so you can glance at it comfortably while you give your presentation.

Giving a Coherent Presentation

Introduction

- Identify health topic
    1. Before you start, write the topic of your condition/disease on the board. Add any other essential terminology related to your condition on the board, too.
    2. Begin your presentation by first pointing to the topic on the board, and then introducing it with a sign, an invented sign, fingerspelling, or an abbreviation of the word.
    3. Next, use a rhetorical question "What is it?", and then tell what that condition is related to. For example, diabetes is a condition related to sugar in the blood, and Parkinson's disease is a condition related to movements of the body.

Diabetes is a condition related to sugar in the blood.

4. Describe symptoms of the condition by asking with a rhetorical question what the person with that disease feels or looks like. Using diabetes as an example, you can explain that a person with diabetes may have experienced fatigue, irritability, excessive thirst, dizziness, or blurred eyesight. Here you can use role shift to demonstrate how a person feels or acts when s/he has that disease. Remember to convert information into verb phrases for ASL.

Body

Begin the body of your presentation with this rhetorical question to talk about what happens inside the body.

- Describe the normal process
  1. You need to describe the normal process of the body parts involved. Use this rhetorical phrase to begin the description.

  2. Now describe how the body normally functions without the disease/condition. For people not affected by diabetes, you can discuss this:

     The body digests food in the stomach converting it into sugar called glucose. The sugar is absorbed through the walls and enters the blood stream. The pancreas gauges how much sugar is in the blood and makes insulin. Then the body gets the energy it needs to function normally.

(We suggest using the imagery of insulin as holding the key to open body cells to allow sugar to come in, or the imagery of insulin capturing sugar, breaking it down, and bringing it to body cells.)

- Describe how the process is affected
  1. Begin discussing how the process is affected with the following rhetorical question.

2. Explain how the normal process or functions are changed/affected by the condition/disease. For diabetes, you can describe this:

Repeat parts of the digestive system that are involved in the process. Show how the sugar gets into the bloodstream, but this time describe the sugar looking for the insulin (with keys) without any success. The doors to the body cells are locked to the sugars, or the insulin "cops" are searching but overlooking them. Then the body becomes weak or tired.

- Tell the cause(s)
  1. Begin discussing causes with this rhetorical question.

2. This is where you explain what caused the condition/disease. Some examples are catching a contagious disease through the air or through physical contact, health affected by unsanitary conditions, lack of proper nutrition, lack of sleep and rest, hazardous environmental factors such as exposure to toxic chemicals, water and air pollution, and finally, hereditary factors.

For diabetes, you can discuss these causes:

Type I: unknown

Type II: hereditary, obesity, pregnancy

Remember to adapt noun phrases, making them action verbs (see notes on page 166–167).

- Discuss treatment(s)
  1. Refer to "Discuss Treatment Options," page 167–169, to determine what phrase/sign most appropriately fits your condition. Utilize the rhetorical question and appropriate phrase/signs learned previously.

  2. On your weak hand, list treatment options (if there are too many, pick several common or useful options). When listing, use raised eyebrows each time you point to the finger on your weak hand to begin describing that option.

For diabetes these treatment options are available.

- *Insulin (ICL"put syringe in stomach or on thigh again and again")*
- *Diet*
- *If blood sugar is low, eat something, or quickly eat a small amount of carbohydrates/sugar*

  3. Refer to page 169–170 for ways of handling medication terminology. You may need to do additional research on the medication specific to your presentation. You must mention the form in which each medication is taken and it purpose.

Conclusion
- Give conclusion
  1. A number of devices will work here. A couple of ideas you could use are sharing prevention techniques or sharing interesting facts like how many people have the condition and who is most affected by it. You can elaborate by naming famous people who have the disease.
  2. Follow up with two or three questions that touch upon key information covered in the presentation. Don't ask questions that require the student to recall a specific fact like numbers or spelling of words. Ask questions that involve general understanding of the information presented, e.g., what population tends to be affected by the illness rather than what percentage have the illness. Time used to ask follow-up questions is *in addition* to the 5-minute time limit for the presentation.

Rehearse Your Presentation

Practice your presentation from your outline. Make sure you are able to complete the presentation in five minutes. Review "Tips for Making a Presentation" on the next page and stand to practice your material.

Tips for Making a Presentation

- Stand in the center of the "stage," body facing forward so it will be easier to look at the entire audience.
- Keep your shoulders back and down in a relaxed position. Hunching your shoulders or pulling them up makes you sign smaller.
- During any long pauses before, during, and after the presentation, keep your hands in a rested position at your waist. Don't let your hands fall limp.
- Use pauses to give emphasis to certain parts and to make transitions clear.
- Never break eye contact with the audience. Glance around, making eye contact with as many audience members as possible. Take note of audience response. Elaborate on parts until you obtain the needed response.
- Don't chew gum.
- If your hair tends to fall in your eyes, pin it back or wear it in a ponytail.
- Wear solid colored clothes. Don't wear clothes with busy backgrounds like plaids or stripes. Your clothes should contrast with the color of your hands.

STORYTELLING

In Deaf culture, storytelling skills are highly valued. You are expected to develop an ability to tell stories as well. In this unit we use fairytales and folktales. These types of stories allow you to use your imagination and lend themselves nicely to character development. They provide you with opportunities to identify basic ASL storytelling techniques. They give you the forum to introduce and practice a more formal presentation. There is nothing more rewarding than presenting a well-told story and nothing more entertaining than seeing one.

Goal of the Unit

This unit will introduce key elements used in ASL storytelling and to show how to adapt literature (written stories) so that you can present an ASL version of a story to the class.

ASSIGNMENT

Choosing a Story

Instructions   Your final project for this unit is to tell a 7- to 10-minute story. Follow the guidelines below to select three appropriate stories to submit to the teacher for his/her approval.

Many things can serve as a source for your storytelling presentation: folktales, fairytales, children's books, short stories, stories from the Bible, or traditional stories from other cultures.

The following stories will be discussed and analyzed in class and cannot be used as your story; "The Frog Prince," "The Bridge of Magpies," "The Merchant's Daughter and the Slanderer," "The Magic Mirror of Rabbi Adam," and "The Twelve Dancing Princesses."

There are some types of stories you should avoid. Do not use sound-based books (like Dr. Seuss books), poems, or sound-based fables. Avoid these elementary fairytales "Three Little Pigs," "Little Red Riding Hood," "Goldilocks and the Three Bears," and "Three Billy Goats Gruff," or any type of "chain" stories such as "One Fine Day," "The Sky Is Falling," or "The Little Red Hen," in which similar actions are repeated throughout the story.

Choose a story that:
- has one main storyline
- has three or more characters
- takes place in at least two different locations and occurs over a period of at least two days
- is sufficiently challenging, not too easy or too hard
- is 7 to 10 minutes long (no more no less).

Timeline

Submit three story cards.   Date: _____

Submit a videotaped story draft.   Date: _____

(In class you are to videotape a draft of your story for your teacher's feedback. You can videotape your story at home provided that you submit the video on this date.)

Present your story.   Date: _____

Story Cards

Instructions   You are to prepare three story cards and submit them to your teacher.

Prepare a story card for each story (8-½" x 11" pages are fine). Identify which of the three stories you prefer to tell. The teacher will confirm your choice, or if needed, suggest another story.

On each story card, include the following:

1. the name of story
2. the source
3. a summary of the story
4. a list of characters (including some description of the characters)
5. opening and closing sentences
6. any special features, words, refrains, or images essential to the story, for example:
     (special words)"abracadabra"
     (refrains)"little pig, little pig, let me in"
     (images) a description of the "Emerald City" in "The Wizard of Oz"
7. tell why you like the story

Sample Story Card

1. *Name of story*—"The Twelve Dancing Princesses"—English fairytale
2. *Source*—B. Hayes, Folktales and Fables of the World, Barnes and Noble, NY, 1995
3. *Summary*—A king with 12 beautiful daughters is very protective of them. To safeguard them he locks them into their room each night, but every morning he discovers their shoes are all worn out. The daughters decline to tell their father where they go each night, so the king offers one of his daughters' hands in marriage to the man who can find out the secret. Many try and fail until one day a soldier, with the help of an old woman's magic, is able to discover the secret. He gets to choose his wife and they live happily ever after.
4. *Characters*—
     a. soldier—poor, humble, and a bit clever
     b. oldest Princess—arrogant, self-centered
     c. youngest Princess—sensitive
     d. king—honest, loves his daughters
     e. old woman—unassuming, clever
5. *Opening*—"Once upon a time, there lived a king who had 12 beautiful daughters."
     Closing—"And they lived happily ever after."
6. *Special features*—requires the use of plural classifiers to describe the actions and possessions of the 12 princesses
7. I like the descriptive elements in the story and the challenge of showing the actions of a group.

Identifying Scenes

Instructions   To begin the process of adapting a written story for a signed presentation, divide "The Twelve Dancing Princesses" (pages 198–200) into scenes. Each scene will serve as the framework for deciding the placement and movements of the characters.

First, read the entire story and then draw a line to separate the Introduction, the Body, and the Conclusion of the story.

Now divide each section into scenes. Use this definition to help you decide where to make the divisions.

"A scene is a part of a story that occurs in a specific location at a specific time; any change in location and/or time marks a new scene."

Use a pencil so you can reconsider your decision when you discuss your divisions in class.

"The Twelve Dancing Princesses"

Once upon a time there was a king who had twelve beautiful daughters. They slept in twelve beds in a single room. The king was jealous of his daughters and each night the door to their room was shut and bolted, but each morning when he unlocked the door, he noticed that their shoes had been danced to pieces, and nobody could explain how it happened. The king declared that if any man discovered the secret of the worn-out shoes he could choose whichever princess he wanted for his wife. But whoever failed after three days would be put to death.

A king's son took up the challenge. In the evening of his arrival he was taken to the anteroom next to the princesses, to keep watch. His bed was made up there, and so that they could not do anything or leave without being seen, the door of the room was left open. But the eyes of the prince grew heavy and he fell asleep. In the morning he found the princesses' shoes full of holes. The same thing happened the second night and again the third night. The prince was then granted no mercy, and the king ordered the prince's head to be cut off. Other princes came but the same thing happened to all of them.

Now it happened that a poor soldier, who had been wounded and could no longer serve, found himself on the road to town where the king lived. There he fell in with an old woman who asked him where he intended to go. "I really don't know," he said, and he added in fun, " but I want to discover where the princesses dance and after that I should like to become king."

"Well, that is not so difficult," said the old woman. "You must not drink the wine which the princesses will give you in the evening, and you must pretend to fall asleep." Whereupon she gave him a short cloak, saying, "When you wear this you will be invisible, and then you can slip out after the twelve princesses."

When the soldier heard the good advice he considered it seriously, plucked up with courage to appear before the king, and offer himself as a suitor. He was as well received as the others and was dressed in royal garments.

In the evening, when bedtime came, he was conducted to the anteroom. As he was about to go to bed the eldest princess appeared, bringing him a cup of wine. Secretly, he threw the wine away, then he lay down, and began to snore as though in deepest sleep.

The twelve princesses heard him and laughed. The eldest said, "He too must forfeit his life."

Then they got up, opened cupboards, chests, and cases, and brought out their beautiful dresses. They decked themselves before the glass, skipping about and reveling in the prospect of the dance.

Only the youngest sister said, "I don't know what it is. You may rejoice, but I feel so uneasy."

"You are a little goose," answered the eldest. "You are always frightened. Have you forgotten how many have come here in vain? Why, even without our sleeping potion the soldier would have slept soundly."

When they were all ready they looked in on the soldier to see that his eyes were shut and he did not stir. The eldest went up to one of the beds and knocked on it. It sank into the earth and they descended through the opening one after another, the eldest first.

The soldier, who had noticed everything, did not hesitate long, but threw on his cloak and went down behind the youngest. In the middle of the stairway he accidentally trod on the gown of the youngest princess. She was frightened and said, "What was that? Who is holding on to my dress?"

"Don't be foolish. You must have caught it on a nail," said the eldest.

At the bottom of the stairs they found themselves at the entrance to a most delightful avenue of trees whose leaves were of glittering silver.

The soldier thought, "I must take some token with me." And he broke off the twig, a sharp crack came: "I am sure all is not right," wailed the youngest, "did you not hear the noise?"

"It is only the sound of the fairy prince shouting for joy at our approach," countered the eldest.

Next they came to an avenue where all the leaves were of gold and to a third whose leaves were of glittering diamonds. From both the soldier broke off a twig, and there was a crack each time, which made the youngest princess start with terror.

Finally they reached a great lake where twelve little boats waited with twelve handsome princes in them. Into each boat stepped one of the sisters. The soldier joined the youngest princess and her prince and as they rowed across the lake the prince remarked: "I do not know why it is, but though I am rowing with all my might the boat feels heavy and I am quite tired."

"I wonder why it is," said the youngest, "unless perhaps it is the hot weather. It is strangely hot."

On the opposite side of the lake stood a splendid brightly lighted castle from which came the sound of joyous music of trumpets and drums. They rowed across, and every prince danced with his princess. And the soldier danced too, unseen. If one of the princesses held a cup of wine he drank out of it, so that it was empty when she lifted it to her lips. This frightened the youngest but the eldest always silenced her.

They danced until dawn when their shoes were quite worn out. The princes took them back across the lake, and this time the soldier took the seat beside the eldest. On the bank they said farewell to their princes and promised to come again the next night.

When the tired princesses approached the secret stairway, the soldier ran on before them and lay down on his bed. The twelve came lagging by, slowly and wearily, he began to snore again very loud, so that they said, "We are quite safe so far as he is concerned." Then they took off their beautiful gowns, put them away, placed the worn-out shoes under their beds, and lay down to sleep.

The next morning the soldier determined to say nothing, but to see the wonderful doings again. So he went with them the second and third nights. Everything was just the same as the first night, and they danced each time till their shoes were in holes. The third time the soldier took away with him a wine cup as a token.

When the appointed hour came for him to answer, he took with him the three twigs and the cup with him and went before the king. The twelve princesses stood behind the door listening to hear what he would say.

When the king put the question, "Where did my daughters dance their shoes to pieces in the night?" he answered, "With twelve princes in an underground castle." Then he produced the tokens.

The king sent for his daughters and ask them whether the soldier spoke the truth. As they saw that they were betrayed and would gain nothing by lies, they were obliged to admit all.

Thereupon the king asked the soldier which one he would choose as his wife. He answered, "I am no longer young so I will have the eldest."

So the wedding was celebrated that very day, and thus the soldier became an heir to a great kingdom. The two of them lived happily ever after.

ASSIGNMENT

Translating Passages

Instructions   Read the whole story and think about how to translate the numbered passages in bold.

"The Merchant's Daughter and the Slanderer"

Once there was a merchant who had two children, a daughter and a son. When the merchant was on his deathbed (his wife had been taken to the graveyard before him) he said, "My children, live well with each other, in love and concord, just as I lived with your deceased mother." Then he died. He was buried and prayers were said for the repose of his soul, as is fitting.

Shortly afterward, the merchant's son decided to trade beyond the sea. He rigged up three ships, loaded them with a variety of goods, and said to his sister, "Now, my beloved sister, I am going on a long voyage and leaving you at home all alone. Mind you, behave properly, do not engage in evil things, and do not consort with strangers." Then they exchanged portraits; the sister took her brother's portrait, the brother took his sister's. They wept as they took leave of each other and said farewell.

The merchant's son raised anchor, pushed off from shore, hoisted sail, and reached the open sea. He sailed for one year, he sailed for another year, and in the third year he came to a certain wealthy capital and anchored his ships in the port. As soon as he arrived he took a bowl full of precious stones and rolls of his best velvet, damask, and satin, and took them to the king of those parts as a gift. He came to the palace, gave his gift to the king, and petitioned for leave to trade in his capital.

(1)   **The precious gift was to the king's liking and he said to the merchant's son, "Your gift is munificent; in all my life I have never received a finer one. In return I grant you the first place on the market. Buy and sell, fear no one, and if anyone injures you, come straight to me. Tomorrow I myself will visit your ship."**

Next day the king came to the merchant's son, began to walk on his ship and examine his goods, and in the master's cabin saw a portrait hanging on the wall. He asked the merchant's son, "Whose portrait is that?"

"My sister's, Your Majesty."

"Well, Mr. Merchant, such a beauty I have not seen in all my days. Tell me the truth: what is her character and what are her manners?"

"She is quiet and chaste as a dove."

"Well, if so, she will be a queen; I will take her to wife."

At that time, a certain general who was spiteful and envious was with the king; at the thought that anyone else might find happiness he choked with rage. He heard the king's words and became terribly angry. "Now," he thought, "our wives will have to bow to a woman of the merchant class!" He could not restrain himself and said to the king, "Your Majesty, do not order me to be put to death, order me to speak."

"Speak."

(2) **"This merchant's daughter is not a suitable match for you. I met her long ago, and more than once I lay on the bed and played amorous games with her. She is quite a dissolute girl."**

"How can you, foreign merchant, say that she is quiet and chaste as a dove, and that she never engages in evil things?"

"Your Majesty, if the general is not lying, let him get my sister's ring from her and find out what is her secret mark."

"Very well," said the king, and he gave the general a furlough. "If you fail to get the ring and tell me the secret mark by such and such a day, your head shall fall by my sword."

(3) **The general made ready and went to the town where the merchant's daughter lived; he arrived and did not know what to do. He walked back and forth in the streets, low in spirits and thoughtful. He happened to meet an old woman who begged for alms; he gave her something. She asked, "What are you thinking about?"**

"Why should I tell you? You cannot help me in my trouble."

"Who knows? Perhaps I can help you."

"Do you know where such and such a merchant's daughter lives?"

"Of course I do."

"If so, get me her ring and find out what is her secret mark. If you do this for me, I shall reward you with gold."

(4) **The old woman hobbled to the merchant's daughter, knocked at her door, said that she was going to the Holy Land, and asked for alms. She spoke so cunningly that the lovely maiden became quite bewitched and did not realize that she had blurted out where her secret mark was; and while all this talk was going on, the old woman slipped the girl's ring from the table and hid it in her sleeve.** Then, she said farewell to the merchant's daughter and ran to the general. She gave him the ring and said, "Her secret mark is a golden hair under her left arm."

The general rewarded her liberally and set out on his way back. He came to his kingdom and reported to the palace; and the merchant's son was there too.

"Well," asked the king, "have you got the ring?"

"Here it is, Your Majesty."

"And what is the merchant's daughter's secret mark?"

"A golden hair under her left arm."

"Is this correct?" asked the king of the merchant's son.

"It is, Your Majesty."

"Then, how dare you lie to me? For this I will order you put to death."

"Your Majesty, do not refuse me one favor. Give me leave to write a letter to my sister; let her come and say farewell to me."

"Very well," said the king, "write to her, but I won't wait long." He postponed the execution and in the meantime ordered that the young man be put in chains and thrown into a dungeon.

(5) **The merchant's daughter, upon receiving her brother's letter, set out immediately. As she traveled she knitted a golden glove and wept bitterly; her tears fell as diamonds, and she gathered these diamonds and studded the glove with them.** She arrived in the capital, rented an apartment in the house of a poor widow, and asked, "What is the news in your city?"

"There is no news except that a foreign merchant is being made to suffer because of his sister. Tomorrow he will be hanged."

Next morning the merchant's daughter arose, hired a carriage, donned a rich garment, and went to the square. There the gallows was ready, troops were standing guard, and a great multitude of people had gathered; and now they led out her brother. She got out of the carriage, went straight to the king, handed him the glove that she had knitted on her way, and said, "Your Majesty, I beg of you, estimate what such a glove is worth."

The king examined it. "Ah," he said, "it is priceless!"

"Well, your general was in my house and stole a glove exactly like it, the other of the pair. Please order that a search be made for it."

The king summoned the general, and said to him, "There is a complaint against you that you stole a precious glove." The general began to swear that he knew nothing about it.

"What do you mean, you don't know?" said the merchant's daughter. "You have been in my house so many times, lain with me on the bed, played amorous games with me."

"But I have never seen you before! I have never been in your house, and not for anything in the world could I say at this moment who you are or whence you have come."

"If so, Your Majesty, why is my brother made to suffer?"

"Which brother?" asked the king.

"The one who is now being led to the gallows."

Thus the truth became known. The king ordered the merchant's son to be released and the general to be hanged; and himself sat in the carriage with the lovely maiden, the merchant's daughter, and drove to the church. They married, made a great feast, began to live in happiness and prosperity, and are still living to this very day.

Exercise 1: Repeated Sequence of Actions

Instructions   Often fairy tales use a repeated sequence of actions as a device to help build suspense and prepare the listener for the climax of the story. With that in mind, your teacher will lead you in a discussion of ways to translate these segments taken from "The Twelve Dancing Princesses."

Segment 1

...each night the door to their room was shut and bolted, but each morning when he unlocked the door, he noticed that their shoes had been danced to pieces...

Segment 2

A king's son took up the challenge. In the evening of his arrival he was taken to the anteroom next to the princesses, to keep watch. His bed was made up there, and so that they could not do anything or leave without being seen, the door of the room was left open. But the eyes of the prince grew heavy and he fell asleep. In the morning he found the princesses' shoes full of holes. The same thing happened the second night and again the third night. The prince was then granted no mercy, and the King ordered the prince's head to be cut off...

Segment 3

...Other princes came but the same thing happened to all of them.

Segment 4

At the bottom of the stairs they found themselves at the entrance to a most delightful avenue of trees whose leaves were of glittering silver.

The soldier thought, "I must take some token with me." And he broke off the twig, a sharp crack came: "I am sure all is not right," wailed the youngest, "did you not hear the noise?"

"It is only the sound of the fairy prince shouting for joy at our approach," countered the eldest.

Next they came to an avenue where all the leaves were of gold and to a third whose leaves were of glittering diamonds. From both the soldier broke off a twig, and there was a crack each time which made the youngest princess start with terror.

Segment 5

...So he went with them the second and third nights. Everything was just the same as the first night, and they danced each time till their shoes were in holes. The third time the soldier took away with him a wine cup as a token.

Repeated Sequence of Actions

To review your classroom discussion here is a summary of how to handle a repeated sequence of actions when it appears in a story. The following discussion is based on the segments listed on page 204.

Segment 1: Time Signs

Time signs modified with either a "sweep" or repeated movement indicate that something occurs regularly.

every night

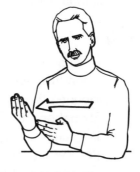

every morning

everyday; on a daily basis

every week

Add this sign to express frustration about a situation that has not changed despite efforts to do so.

situation remains unchanged

Segment 2: Condensing

This segment tells what happened to the prince each night for three nights. The written English version condenses the information by saying "The same thing happened the second night and again the third night." To condense the information in ASL, use the following strategy.

- For the first night, give a full description.
- For the second night, begin with the phrase below. Follow with a shorter description of the same actions, but eliminate some details, use minimal role shift, and sign faster. Conclude by using the sign below on the right to indicate everything remained the same or unchanged.

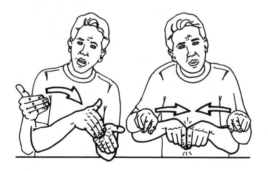

- For the third night, sign faster, delete more details, keep only the most essential information, use no role shift. Begin and end the third night with the same phrase listed above.

Segment 3: Verb Inflections for Number and Frequency

To show that something happened to an unspecified number of people over a period of time, you can inflect verbs to show repetition across the sign space. In "The Twelve Dancing Princesses" the scene shows that different men at different times came, tried, failed, and subsequently were beheaded. The sign illustrated below is inflected to show that several men tried over a period of time.

Segment 4: Expansion

Because new information is added each time the soldier entered the next avenue of trees, don't condense the information. Instead, expand each scene by intensifying the reactions of the soldier and the youngest daughter to create interest and to build suspense.

Segment 5: Condensing

This is similar to Segment 2 where you need to describe in detail what happens on the first night and then reduce the amount of details given for the second and third nights.

Exercise 2: Presenting the Story Title

Instructions   Follow the guidelines to help you present your story title.

- Translate the title word for word.
- Spell the title from your nondominant side to your dominant side.
- If a word in the title corresponds to a sign, sign it out.
  For example: "My Daughter." Both words in the title would be signed.
- If there is no corresponding sign, spell it out.
  For example: "The Beauty and the Beast." Everything is spelled out except the word "and," which is signed.
- If the sign is not specific enough, then give the sign followed by fingerspelling to clarify.
  For example: "The Sparrow." Spell "the," use the sign for "bird," and then spell out "sparrow."
- If the title is very long such as "How the Giraffe Got His Long Neck and Why the Rhinoceros Is So Grumpy," visually break the title into two "lines" in the signing space.
  For example: (Line 1) How the Giraffe Got His Long Neck
                 (Line 2) And Why the Rhinoceros Is So Grumpy
- Use this sign before or after giving the title.

Practice translating the following titles, keeping in mind the guidelines discussed above.

1. "Rumpelstiltskin"
2. "The Emperor's New Clothes"
3. "The Eagle and the Rabbit"
4. "Goldilocks and the Three Bears"
5. "The Twelve Dancing Princesses"

Giving a Story Summary

Instructions   You are to prepare a summary of your story to present to the class. Use the following guidelines to help you develop your summary.

Guidelines for Giving a Summary

- Give the title.
- Begin the summary with the phrase "STORY ABOUT…."
- Tell only the basic storyline. Give only the essential information. Don't give descriptions unless they are needed to understand the basic plot.
- For parts of the story where actions are repeated, describe the first night, and then just say "second night and third night same thing happened."
- Don't use role shift, and don't include dialogue.
- Rather than assigning name signs or fingerspelling names, it is better to refer to them simply by identifying them using basic nouns as the girl, the boy, the king, the bird, the monster, or the witch.
- However, if the name itself plays an important role in the story, you can spell the name or assign a name sign. For example, in the story "Rapunzel" the name plays an important role throughout the story. First, it is the name of the lettuce in the witch's garden; second, the witch names the baby after the lettuce when she takes the baby from the couple; third, the witch and later the prince call "Rapunzel, Rapunzel, let down your hair" to get access to the tower. In this case, you would spell out the name or assign a name sign.

Summary "The Twelve Dancing Princesses"

View. John will use the class story "The Twelve Dancing Princesses" to demonstrate how to summarize a story using the guidelines listed above.

Key Elements

In developing your story, incorporate the following key elements to help you tell an interesting, easy to follow, and—most importantly—enjoyable story.

Placement of Characters

Since you are required to have three or more characters in your story, the placement of those characters throughout the story will take some planning. Place the main character on your dominant side and place the second most significant character on your nondominant side. Be sure this placement is consistent throughout the story. Things related to the character, such as his/her castle or home, should be placed on the same side as the character. For example, in the story "The Frog Prince" the "princess" would be placed on your dominant side and the "frog" on the other side (see the illustration below).

Placing Two Characters

Character 1
(dominant side)

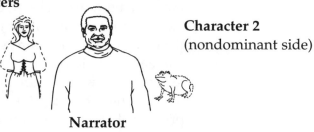

Character 2
(nondominant side)

Narrator
(Reverse sides if you are left-handed)

When you role shift between the characters, your eye gaze should agree with the character's placement. For example, if you role shift to show the character on your right side speaking to another character on the left, your eye gaze should be directed at that character on the left. Then when you role shift to show the other character's response, shift positions so that your eye gaze is directed to the character on the right.

When you introduce a third character in your story, you need to determine their relationship to the first two characters. For example, in "The Frog Prince," the king as a third character deals primarily with the princess on the right, so he enters from the right and "pushes" the princess to the left for their interaction.

Character 3
(appears on
the right side)

Character 1
(moves from the right side
to center and left side of king)

Character 2
(remains on
left side)

Narrator

There may be times in the story when it is logical to change the placement of the character either because a change in the location makes for a smoother transition to the next scene or because a change logically follows what was said or done in the previous scene. For example, consider the scene in Ben's story "Rabbi Adam and The Magic Mirror," where the magician orders the rabbi to leave the room while he performs his final magical trick. In this scene, the rabbi comes from the right, passes in front of the magician and exits the room to the left. When the rabbi returns, he is now to the left of the magician. This works because it flows logically from the previous scene.

Another example is from Terrylene's story "The Merchant's Daughter and The Slanderer." In scenes with the king, the general is placed on the right. When the general leaves to travel to the town where the sister lives, he leaves to the right. The general arrives on the left in the sister's town, and remains on the left until he leaves town. Later in the story the sister sets sails to see the king and the general. She arrives from the right and the general is moved to the left of the king. This move makes further sense because in the next scene the king orders the general to take the place of the brother on the gallows, which was established on the left side earlier in the story.

In situations where an authority figure, such as a king, is introduced in the scene, he is usually placed in the center and slightly above the other character(s). In this situation, you need to use an up-down role shift—the character(s) "look up" to the king as he "looks down."

Narrator as king looking down at subject

Narrator as subject looking up at king

Movement

To tell a cohesive story you need to show the movements of characters and/or objects from scene to scene, as well as within a scene.

Movement of Character

There are three techniques you can use to show characters' movement.

Use signs that specifically indicate movements. For example, the following signs state that someone "entered the room," "walked away," or "left home."

- Use classifiers that show characters' movements. For example, SCL:1"*running away or pacing around the room.*" With facial expressions, you can add information about how this person walked or paced the room—slowly, anxiously, or excitedly.
- Use "wandering eye gaze" with role shift. In this case, you role shift to the character to show the character's body swaying slightly from side to side, their eyes wandering as they move from scene to scene or within a scene.

These three techniques are often used in various combinations to describe characters' movements.

View. In the four examples on the video, all three techniques are used to show movement of characters from scene to scene. Read the information about Examples 1–4 before viewing them.

Example 1—In this excerpt from "The Bridge of Magpies," Missy uses classifiers to show the prince riding a horse. Note the movement of the hands and body indicating the forward movement of the horse and the prince. Facial expressions indicate that things are normal.

Example 2—In another excerpt from "The Bridge of Magpies," Missy again uses classifiers to show a flock of birds circling, ascending toward heaven and then building a bridge with their own bodies.

Example 3—In this excerpt from "The Merchant's Daughter and the Slanderer," Terrylene role shifts to the king using the "wandering eye gaze" technique to show that the king is excited as he announces to various people his plans to marry the merchant's daughter.

Example 4—In this excerpt from "The Frog Prince," Ken uses all three techniques: signs indicating "walk" and "going through (forest)," a classifier indicating the path the princess takes through the forest, and "wandering eye gaze" when role shifting to show her carrying the ball as she walks along.

Movement of Object

To show the movement of an object you can:
- use classifiers like LCL (locative classifiers) or SCL (semantic classifiers) to represent the object moving; add facial expressions to show the speed and/or manner in which the object moves.
- use role shift and ICL (instrument classifiers) to show how a character moved an object by throwing, dropping, or passing it.

Note. When you show two characters giving or exchanging an object, you must role shift to both characters and show the object being given and being received. We call this "matching actions." In signing this exchange it is essential to maintain the proper placement of the characters.

View. Here are three examples of how the movement of objects is shown. Read the information about Examples 5-7 before viewing them.

Example 5—In "The Magic Mirror of Rabbi Adam," Ben uses LCL to show how the arrow moved. In order to maintain proper spatial relationships among the characters (the magician and the merchant), he uses his weak (left) hand to trace the arrow's path.

Example 6—In this excerpt from "The Frog Prince," Ken uses a combination of classifiers and facial expressions to show how the princess handled the ball (ICL*"throwing and catching ball with both hands"*) and to show where the ball bounced when she missed it. To show the bouncing, Ken uses LCL:S*"ball on the ground, off the tree, and down the well"* and finally LCL:1*"ball traveling down the well."*

Example 7—In "The Merchant's Daughter and the Slanderer," Terrylene uses matching actions to show the brother and sister exchanging and setting up their pictures. Terrylene maintains the proper placement (brother on left and sister on right) throughout. She uses (2h)LCL:B*"pictures being exchanged"* and then role shifts to the sister and then to the brother, using ICL*"taking the picture and setting it up."* Finally she uses LCL:B to show where each placed their pictures.

Maintain Continuity

To help maintain a sense of continuity as the story progresses, the passage of time must be indicated and accounted for. This can be done with time signs, modified verbs, and transition signs.

Time Signs

Use time signs or phrases to give a specific time (e.g., "one day"), or to jump from one time frame to another (e.g., "that night") or to tell how much time has elapsed (e.g., "for three weeks" or "every morning and every night").

View. Following are four examples of time signs that move stories along. Read the information about Examples 8-11 before viewing them.

Example 8—In this excerpt from "The Frog Prince," after talking about the king's five daughters, Ken uses a time phrase that not only specifies the time but is a traditional phrase used to signal the transition from the Introduction to the Body of the story.

Example 9—In "The Frog Prince," this time phrase, used after describing the frog's emotions, forwards the story to the next night at the castle.

Example 10—In "The Magic Mirror of Rabbi Adam," this time sign is used to show the length of time that passed between one action (the merchant packing up and going home) and another (coming back to town).

Example 11—This excerpt from "The Twelve Dancing Princesses" shows the King coming into the princesses' room every evening to say good night, and returning to the room in the morning. The signer modifies the time signs to indicate that the king's visits to the princesses' room went on for some time.

Modified Verbs

Modify the verb with a repeated circular movement (continuous aspect) to indicate the action lasted over a period of time, e.g., "She cried and cried" or "she mulled it over."

View. Three examples of modified verbs indicating the actions lasting over a period of time. Read the information about Examples 12-14 before viewing them.

Example 12—In "The Bridge of Magpies," we have this example of the two lovers crying so much for so long that it resulted in flooding on earth. To show this intense action occurring over a period of time, Missy modifies the verb "to shed tears" with repeated circular movements (continuous aspect) accompanied by an opening and closing of the mouth in rhythm with the signing and squinted eyes to indicate intensity.

Example 13—In "The Bridge of Magpies," Missy modifies the verb "to rain" (continuous aspect) accompanied by a facial expression that shows this intense action occurred over a period of time.

Example 14—In "The Magic Mirror of Rabbi Adam," Ben describes the rabbi carefully examining the apple tree as he walks around it. In this case, the modified verbs are two classifiers used for "walking around." The classifiers are modified (continuous aspect) and are accompanied by similar but less intense facial expressions.

Transitions

Use transition signs to signal the beginning of a new scene.

View. Here are two examples of transition signs. Read the information about Examples 15 and 16 before viewing them.

Example 15—In this excerpt from "The Frog Prince," Ken describes the princess' delight when the frog left after the first night, only to be upset again the next night. The sign below suggests that the frog's return on the second night is unexpected.

Example 16—This part of "The Magic Mirror of Rabbi Adam" shows the merchant closing up shop and leaving town for his home. The transition sign on the following page indicates the completion of one set of actions (closing up the store) and leads us to the next set of actions (going home).

Character Development

Character development is essential to bring the story to life. A good ASL storyteller develops characters not by using descriptive adjectives to reveal their personalities or their actions, but by role shifting to reflect the character's personality and mood by showing their reactions or feelings as s/he interacts with other characters throughout the story.

To further expand on a character's personality you can vary your signing style to reflect the character's feelings.

- Change the size of the sign (e.g., bigger signs to show an excited character or smaller signs to show a shy, timid character)
- Change the tempo of the sign (e.g., sign deliberately as a wise man would sign, sign fast as a panicked person would sign, or sign slurred to show a character who is groggy or under a spell).
- Exaggerate the sign to reflect strong emotions (e.g., a sign that is normally made on one hand is made with both hands).

Reactions/Comments

View. Five examples of how a character's reactions/comments are shown. Read the information about Examples 17–21 before viewing them.

Example 17—In this excerpt from "The Frog Prince," Ken shows the frog requesting that the princess bring him to her bedroom after he finished eating. Note the tired but content face Ken makes for the frog by making the "mm" mouth (content) and squinted eyes (tired). Ken continues the characterization by using a signing style that is soft and endearing.

Example 18—This segment from "The Bridge of Magpies" shows the king telling the two lovers about his decision to let them meet only one day every year. Missy shows the king's reaction of disappointment before assuming a stern disposition as he explains his decision. Notice that the king's eye gaze maintains the appropriate spatial relationship to the couple. Then, Missy briefly shows the lovers' sad response.

Example 19—Ben shows two different personalities in this part from "The Magic Mirror of Rabbi Adam"—the serious nature of Rabbi Adam and the drunken, careless style of the magician's friends. He does this with his face and by varying his signing styles. The rabbi stands up straight, signs firmly and clearly, and his face is stoic showing a bit of disgust (mouth mostly a small pout and eyebrows a bit furrowed). The friends are drunk and sway their heads, a pursed mouth reflecting carelessness and indifference. Their signing is sloppy, not crisp.

Example 20—In "The Merchant's Daughter and the Slanderer," Terrylene shows the reactions and comments of three men (the general, the king, and the merchant's son). Using effective role shifting techniques and appropriate eye gaze, she shows the arrogance of the general giving the king the gold ring and explaining the secret mark of the merchant's daughter, the king's confusion, concern and then anger with the merchant's son; and the merchant's son's dismay.

Example 21—In "The Merchant's Daughter and the Slanderer," Terrylene shows the king's surprise when he hears the merchant's daughter reveal who she is. The king turns to the general (on his left) and accuses him of lying. Note that the sign for "lying" is exaggerated to show the king's anger.

Thoughts

Another way to develop character is to show the character's thoughts. In doing this we show the character's desires and subsequent motives for his/her actions. There are two ways to reflect the characters' thoughts.
- While role shifting, break eye contact, shifting the gaze up and away to give the impression that the character is not relating directly to the other character in the scene.
- A more subtle way does not divert the eye gaze away from the other character—instead the signer reduces the character's head movement to almost nothing and signs low and small, giving the impression that the character is not relating to the other character in the scene.

View. Four examples of how a character's thoughts are shown. Pay particular attention to the character's eye gaze in all examples. Read the information about Examples 22–25 before viewing them.

Example 22—In this segment from "The Frog Prince," Ken tells us about the princess' "thoughts" as she looks away from the well. While the eye gaze moves up, Ken uses a sign to signal the beginning of the princess' thoughts. When the princess finishes her thought about a promise, Ken reverses the sign movement to reflect the end of the thought and has her resume looking down at the well.

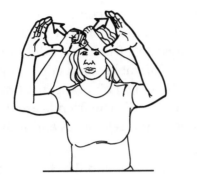

signals beginning of thought

signals end of thought

Example 23—In this excerpt from "The Bridge of Magpies," Missy shows the king's thoughts after receiving the prince's request to marry his daughter. The king's eye gaze is on the prince kneeling in front of him, then he breaks eye contact to ponder the riches the prince has and how close he lives to the king. Note that the signing is lower and more subtle than when the king spoke directly to the prince.

Example 24—In this excerpt from "The Merchant's Daughter and the Slanderer," Terrylene shows the beggar woman's restrained excitement on discovering the secret mark. Terrylene shows the beggar woman continually looking at the daughter, signing low to herself, "Oh boy, that's it!" She looks toward the audience, saying "That's her secret mark!" and then returns her eye gaze to the daughter.

Example 25—The thoughts of the magician from "The Magic Mirror of Rabbi Adam" are revealed at the moment he learns that Rabbi Adam had miraculously saved the merchant's life, defying the magician's powers. Ben shows the magician first looking with disbelief at the merchant on his right and then breaking eye gaze off to his left, thinking that now there is someone else who has comparable magical powers, which he resents. The magician returns his gaze on the merchant to offer the challenge.

Special Features

Special features are elements of storytelling that help to add mood and drama to a story, though not all stories lend themselves to these features.

Repeated Sequence (of Actions)

For a discussion of how to analyze and translate story segments with repeated sequence of actions, read the review notes on pages 205–207.

View. Watch three examples of how to show a repeated sequence of actions. Read the information about Examples 26–28 before viewing them.

Example 26—In "The Twelve Dancing Princesses," Anthony modifies verbs to show various men at different times attempting to find the secret only to fail and be beheaded.

Example 27—In "The Twelve Dancing Princesses," Anthony uses "condensing" to describe the actions of the prince during the three nights.

Example 28—In "The Magic Mirror of Rabbi Adam," Ben uses "expansion" to describe the magician's increasing frustration each time the arrow misses the merchant. On the third try, the situation is expanded when the rabbi suggests that the merchant raise his pinky finger so the arrow can "hit" him in order to fool the magician.

Rhythmic Movement

Assigning a certain rhythmic movement to a group of signs can help create a specific mood or state. "The Bridge of Magpies" uses this special feature to highlight its mythical and romantic theme.

View. Two examples from "The Bridge of Magpies" show how signing with certain rhythmic movements establishes a mood. Read the information about Examples 29 and 30 before viewing them.

Example 29—In describing the lovers' idyllic romantic state, Missy uses rhythmic movements from side to side. Note how her mouth moves to coincide with her signing rhythm.

Example 30—In this scene, Missy describes the chaos and destruction taking place on earth after the separation of the lovers. She signs quickly and urgently in this segment to reflect the harshness, turbulence, and the animals' fear and concerns associated with the destruction. Note the facial expression where her mouth is puffed outward and her eyes are squinted. This reflects the intensity of the actions.

Metamorphosis

Many fairytales have an element of magic where things appear, disappear, or are transformed. One way to describe this magic is to simply say that something disappeared or appeared from nowhere using a sign that looks like a whirlwind. This sign can also be used to say that something was transformed suddenly into something else. There is another, more elaborate way of describing a transformation, which is to describe the process of change as it takes place.

View. Observe how these five examples show disappearance, appearance, transformation, and detailed metamorphosis. Read the information about Examples 31–35 before viewing them.

Example 31—In "The 12 Dancing Princesses," the soldier vanishes after putting on the magical cloak to follow the princesses underground. Anthony uses the "whirlwind" sign for this.

Example 32—In "Cinderella," John describes the famous scene where the fairy godmother appears to help Cinderella get ready for the ball. John uses the "whirlwind" sign to signify appearance rather than disappearance.

Example 33—In "The Frog Prince," when the prince describes the curse that made him into a frog, the signer uses the "whirlwind" sign to signify a change in size (to a small frog).

Example 34—In "Snow White," John describes the queen, who after drinking a potion, becomes a hideous looking witch. John shows the metamorphosis: hair sprouting and becoming wild, body increasing in size, the posture becoming bent, and the nose growing large. Note John's facial expressions, particularly his mouth, as he describes the transformation taking place.

Example 35—In this example from "The Magic Mirror of Rabbi Adam," Ben describes the transformation of the magician's staff as it becomes an apple tree. Ben starts with the tree trunk growing bigger, the branches sprouting, the leaves coming out, and then the apples appearing. Ben's mouth matches these changes to express "popping." He reverses the process in a quicker manner when describing the change back into the staff.

Rehearsing "The Twelve Dancing Princesses"

Instructions   Review the following to help you develop the story before rehearsing.

The placement of the main characters

Place the characters as follows:

King—When the king has a conversation with one other character only, place the king directly in front of the other character.

as king addressingthe soldier   *as soldier addressingthe king*

In cases where the king addresses two other characters, as in the final scene, the king should be placed in the middle, addressing the soldier on the right and the princesses on the left.

soldier to the right of king   *king in the middle*   *princesses to the left of king*

Soldier—The main character, the soldier, should be placed on your dominant side (assuming the right side). The character should remain there throughout the story.

Princesses—Thus, the princesses should be placed on the left throughout the story.

Once you place your characters, the principals of role shift learned in Unit 18 apply.

Movements of characters

To describe the movement of the twelve princesses, use plural classifier (PCL:4) to show them gathering in a group and then hurrying in a line along the avenues of trees on their way to the underground castle. In contrast, use SCL:1*"one person moving"* to show the soldier following the princesses. Show the character's mood or attitude on your face and in your signing pace For example, the princesses being excited as they go through the trees and exhausted upon their return home.

Maintain story continuity

To maintain continuity you must account for the passage of time within the story.
- Use specific time signs to indicate the next day, the next morning, the second or third night.
- Inflect verb signs to show that the activity went on for some time. For example, inflect the sign "dance" with continuous aspect to show the princesses dancing all night.

Handling repeated sequence of actions

There are several segments in the story where actions are repeated. See Review Notes: Repeated Sequence of Actions, pages 205–207, to refresh your memory on how to translate these segments.

Development of characters

There are several characters in this story. Their personalities can come alive when you tell a good deal of the story in role shift. Take time to develop the attitudes, actions, and thoughts of the soldier, the youngest princess, and the oldest princess.

Plurality

Throughout the story, a number of references are made to the twelve princesses' possessions, actions, and movements as a group. To effectively show plurality you can state a number, modify the noun, verb, or classifier by repeating the sign, or use a plural classifier. Review the list below and incorporate the different ways to show plurality in the story.

twelve daughters

twelve beds in one room

pairs of shoes under the beds

pairs of shoes worn out

princesses getting dressed for the dance

princesses filing down through the secret passageway

three avenues of trees

princes waiting inside the boats

princesses getting in the boats

boats going across the lake

musicians playing trumpets and drums

princes and princesses dancing

princesses saying farewell to the princes

princesses getting into bed

princesses at door eavesdropping on the soldier and the king

princesses standing in the room with the soldier and the king

Now you are ready to rehearse the story. Make sure the sequence of events is logical and clear and stay within the 7- to 10-minute limit. Be prepared to tell the story next class.

Preparing Your Story

Preparing the Story for Adaptation

- After reading your story, try to visualize the action.
- Reread the story. Check to see if you have missed any details that you feel are essential.
- Divide your story into scenes and memorize the actions. Adapt the conversations and thoughts of the characters.

Make notes of any special words, descriptions, and images or refrains essential to the story. Think about how to translate them.

Review

Read Review Notes: Key Elements, pp. 210–220, and Review Notes: Repeated Sequence of Actions, pp. 205–207.

Ways to Begin and End a Story

There are different ways to begin and end a story. Choose the ending that best suits your story.

If your story is a straightforward fairytale like "The Twelve Dancing Princesses," which begins with something like "Once upon a time..." and ends with something like "and they lived happily ever after," use the following common translations.

Begin: "Once upon a time..."

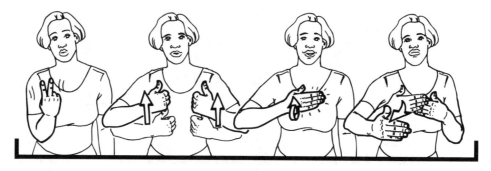

End: "And they both lived happily every after..."

If your story ends with a moral or a lesson to remember, use one of these phrases to transition to your concluding remarks.

End: "the moral is..."

End: "the moral is..."

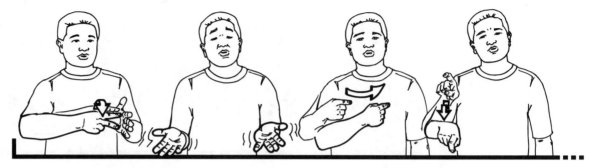

End: "the moral is..."

If your story is about the origin of things or why things are the way they are, like "The Bridges of Magpies," use the following to begin and conclude your remarks:

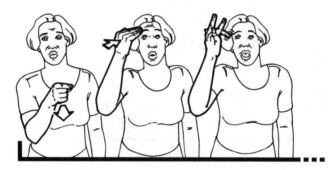

Begin: "Do you know how come...(such and such)"

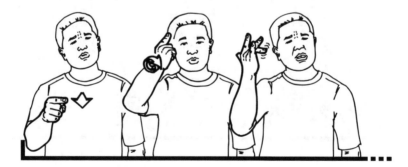

Begin: "Do you ever wonder why...(such and such)"

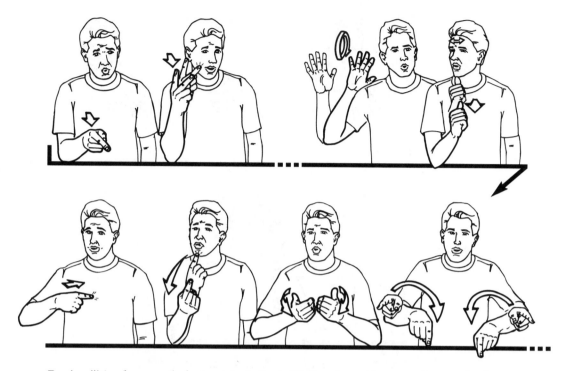

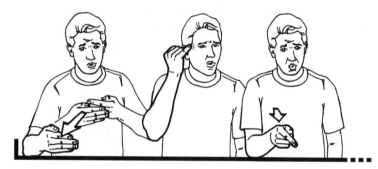

Begin: "You know... (what exists today). Well, a long time ago, it wasn't that way. Let me tell you what happened."

End: "and now, if you..."

End: "and that's why...(such and such is the way it is)"

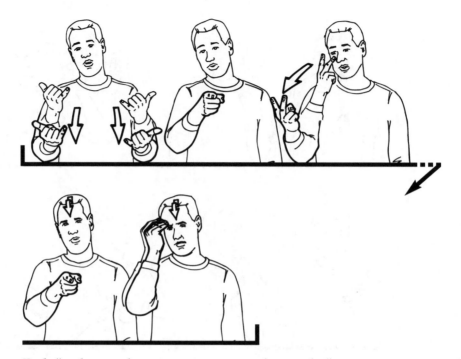

End: "and now whenever you see..., you know why"

The Very End   After concluding a live presentation, as opposed to a videotaped presentation, close by fingerspelling "The End." (Spell it across the sign space as you would a title. See page 208 for how to present titles.) Make eye contact with the whole audience and nod to acknowledge the audience's reaction to the story.

Presenting the Story Live

Stance/Composure
- Stand in the center of the "stage," body facing forward so it will be easier to look at the entire audience. Position yourself just outside of the "arc" of students.

- Stand squarely on both feet. Don't shift your body weight to one foot.
- Keep your head up and your face forward
- Keep your shoulders back and down in a relaxed position. Hunching your shoulders or pulling them up makes you sign smaller.
- Keep your elbows away from your body. Use your whole arms when you sign not just your forearms. This will result in bigger and clearer signs.
- Just before you begin your story, stand erect with your arms down at your side. Glance around to make sure you have everyone's attention then give the title. When you fingerspell the title keep the passive arm down at your side.
- During any long pauses in your story, keep your hands closed together in a rested position at your waist. Don't let your hands fall limp.

rest position during a long pause

Movement
- Don't add movements (of your hands, head, or body) that are not related to the story or to the signs themselves, e.g., swaying body, bouncing, adjusting your clothes, or scratching your nose.
- Don't move feet from their position unless necessary for the story.

When using role shift, turn your head and/or body to a 45° angle in either direction so the audience can see 3/4 of your face.

Signing Speed/Pace
- Use pauses effectively. Too many will make your presentation choppy. Control pauses to give emphasis to certain parts and to make transitions clear.
- Don't let your signing become rote. Vary the pacing of your signing. Tell the story as if it is your first time telling it. Be enthusiastic, deliberate, and entertaining.

Eye Gaze
- Never break eye contact with the audience except briefly when using role shift. Glance around, making eye contact with as many audience members as possible. Take note of audience response. Elaborate on parts until you obtain the needed response.

Appearance
- Don't chew gum.
- Be sure your hair is held away from your face and pinned in place.
- Wear solid colored clothes. Don't wear clothes with "busy" backgrounds like plaids or stripes. Your clothes should contrast with the color of your hands.

Now rehearse presenting your story incorporating these principles.

SIGNING STORIES

CONTENTS

"A Teacher I'll Never Forget" by Mary Telford

Instructions
- Type the outline and your answers on a separate sheet of paper.
- Develop a detailed outline of the video story.
- If you are unsure about parts of the story, seek help from fellow students, Deaf friends, interpreters—anyone but your teacher.
- Use short sentences or phrases to fill in the answers. Be sure your answer is complete. See example below.

I. **Introduction** (4 points each; 24 points total)
   A. Mary introduces her memorable teacher by naming six facts about her.

Example
     1. *taught at the Texas School for the Deaf-third or fourth grade*

     2.

     3.

     4.

     5.

     6.

II. **Body** (4 points each; 64 points total)
   A. Three ways the teacher compensated for her height. (4 points each)

     1.

     2.

     3.

   B. How the teacher prepared and taught English (3 steps). (4 points each)

     1.

     2.

     3.

   C. Three ways the teacher dealt with her allergy to chalk dust. (4 points each)

     1.

     2.

     3.

D. What happened one time when the teacher left the classroom (7 details).
   (4 points each)

   1.

   2.

   3.

   4.

   5.

   6.

   7.

III. Conclusion (4 points each; 12 points total)

   A. Three ways the teacher is so memorable. (4 points each)

   1.

   2.

   3.

ASSIGNMENT 2

"Never above the Waist" by Cinnie MacDougall

Instructions
- View the video story and answer the questions below.
- Type the questions and your answers on a separate sheet of paper.
- If you are unsure about parts of the story, seek help from fellow students, Deaf friends, interpreters—anyone but your teacher.
- Put an asterisk beside the question that was the most difficult to answer and explain to the teacher why it was difficult.

Introduction (62 points total)
1. The new P.E. teacher is also responsible for what? (4 points)
2. What was the sport? What season is this sport played? (4 points)
3. Who found the equipment? List the equipment they had. In what condition was the equipment? (9 points)
4. The sign, glossed as HAVE, means what? (2 points)
   a. The coach owns the equipment
   b. There is equipment available
5. Why did Cinnie join the new team? (4 points)
6. How many girls signed up for the team? (2 points)
7. How did Cinnie describe the coach's language or communication skills? (5 points)
8. What was the one important rule the coach emphasized? (2 points)
9. What did Cinnie think of the rule? (4 points)
10. How long did Cinnie's team practice before their first game? (2 points)
    a. They practiced for one or two weeks
    b. They practiced for two weeks
11. Compare Cinnie's team and the opposing team in terms of uniform and equipment (Cinnie's team = 2 details; the opposing team = 5 details). (14 points)
12. Even though the Deaf team didn't have fancy equipment and uniforms, what was the deaf girls' attitude toward the game? (4 points)
13. How did Cinnie compare abilities of the two teams? (6 points)

Body (33 points total)
14. What phrase marks the beginning of the body of the story? (2 points)
15. After the last foul play, where did the hearing girl stand to hit the ball into play? (5 points)

16. Which of these did actually happen? Pick more than one if needed. (4 points)

    a. The hearing girl hit the ball back on the ground.

    b. The hearing girl hit the ball high in the air.

    c. Cinnie ran back to hit the ball.

    d. Cinnie held her ground when hitting the ball.

    e. Cinnie intentionally lifted her stick above her waist.

17. Which girl did Cinnie hit with the ball? (5 points)

18. Describe what happened afterward. How did Cinnie feel? What did her coach do? (10 points)

19. What is the best translation of the sign, glossed as LOUSY, given the situation? (2 points)

    a. feel lousy   c. feel like a fool

    b. feel terrible   d. played lousy

20. How did Cinnie interpret the hearing team's dirty looks? (5 points)

Conclusion (5 points total)

21. Translate Cinnie's closing. (5 points)

ASSIGNMENT 3

"A Lesson about Sound" by Mary Telford

Instructions You are to submit a double-spaced typewritten translation of Mary Telford's story. This is a complex assignment that will take a considerable amount of time to complete. You should start as early as possible to get a sense of the task before you. Consider the following process to help you with your translation:

Translation Process

1. Understand the story before you begin your translation. If you are unsure about parts of the story seek help from fellow students, Deaf friends, interpreters—anyone but your teacher.

2. Once you understand the story, write your first draft. Make sure your pronouns correctly reflect which character said what, did what, and thought what. Take care to distinguish between what is said by the narrator and what is said by the characters (expressed through role shift).

3. Write a second draft, making sentences sound smooth and connected. Avoid a miscellaneous assortment of sentences, each stating something but not in a uniform way. Think of accurate, vivid, ways to describe the characters' actions and reactions to make reading the translation interesting and inviting. Keep a dictionary and thesaurus by your side for this assignment.

4. Once you are satisfied with your written translation, ask at least two people to read your paper. One person should be a fellow student working on the same translation. Their feedback will help with accuracy. The other person should be someone who isn't familiar with either ASL or the story. Their feedback will help with the readability of the written English.

5. Underline the parts of the translation you had the most trouble with. At the end of your paper, comment on your process by answering these questions:

   a. How did your translation process differ from the one we suggested?

   b. What difficulties did you have and how did you resolve them?

   c. What did you learn from each of your readers?

   d. What was the most important thing you learned from this exercise?

Your translation will be evaluated on:
- content: accuracy of content (30%)
- style/tone: choice of words, level of detail (30%)
- composition: readability, flow, and coherence (30%)
- comments: your reflections about the process (10%)

"Some Thoughts on Fingerspelling" by Laurene Gallimore

Instructions
- Type the questions and answers on a separate piece of paper.
- When answering the questions, synthesize the information from the video and write a complete answer.

1. Compare how Deaf children learn fingerspelling with how hearing children learn spelling. (10 points)

2. Explain the two types of fingerspelling and give examples. (10 points)

3. What is the partial list of "rules" Laurene presents for fingerspelling in every-day ASL conversations? (10 points)

4. What did Laurene suggest that hearing people do to learn to read fingerspelling more successfully? (10 points)

5. Discuss your experiences learning fingerspelling. How do these experiences support or differ from Laurene's theory and suggestions? (10 points)

"The Whistle Stops the Game" by Marlon Kuntze

Instructions
- View the story and answer the questions below.
- Type the questions and answers on a separate piece of paper.
- If you are unsure about parts of the story, seek help from fellow students, Deaf friends, interpreters—anyone but your teacher.

1. Marlon, as background to his story, describes what is habitually done when the Deaf school has basketball games at home. Summarize the information. (10 points)

2. Identify six signs from the story that are used to indicate these activities are routinely done. (3 points each)

3. What discourse marker is used to begin the "body" of the story. (6 points)

4. Summarize what happened in the "body" of the story. (20 points)

5. Do you think the boy had an ulterior motive for giving Marlon the whistle? Support your position with three examples from the story. (15 points)

6. From the time Marlon blew the whistle and stopped the game to the end of the story, Marlon goes through a series of reactions. The various reactions are listed in the order they appear in the story. Beside each reaction, describe the situation sign expressions, and facial expressions, that coincide with the reaction. (4 points each)

Reaction:

Example   a. Puzzlement—

situation:	just after the whistle was blown, and the game has come to an end
sign:	"5" hand with middle fingers bent-touch and brush up against chest
facial expression:	furrowed eyebrows expressing puzzlement

   b. First realization—

   c. Embarrassment—

   d. Humiliation—

   e. Second realization—

   f. Resolution—

7. All these reactions imply that Marlon did not intend to stop the game. But what is the one sign that clearly states he did not intend to stop the game? Describe the sign. (8 points)

"Ordering at McDonald's" by John Maucere

Instructions You are to submit a double-spaced typewritten translation of John Maucere's story. This is a complex assignment that will take a considerable amount of time to complete. You should start as early as possible to get a sense of the task before you. Consider the following process to help you with your translation:

Translation Process

1. Understand the story before you begin your translation. If you are unsure about parts of the story seek help from fellow students, Deaf friends, interpreters—anyone but the teacher.

2. Go back through the story and identify parts of the story that are not easily translated, such as how to describe the various ways characters in the story communicate; or how to describe the characters' actions and reactions. Keep a dictionary and thesaurus by your side for this assignment.

   Below is a list of fingerspelled words used in the story. We've listed them to help you with recognition.

NTD	Big Mac
Denver	Braille
McDonald's	Helen Keller the second
sun	

   The first part of the story has been translated to set the tone and to help you get started. View the story then try to translate the first part to get an idea of what the task involves. Compare your translation with the one below. Once you feel you understand the task, finish translating the rest of the story.

Introduction:

Sample translation *Whenever I order food at a restaurant, I sign what I want. I refuse to write down my order and apologetically explain that I am deaf. The hearing person would then look down on me and think the problem is mine, not hers. No way! I won't accept that! Hearing and Deaf people have to deal with the communication problem together. That's why I always sign my order.*

3. Once you have a written translation, ask at least two people to read the paper. One person should be a fellow student working on the same translation. Their feedback should help with accuracy. The other person should be someone who isn't familiar with the story, but has a good command of English and writing composition. Their feedback will help with the flow and readability of the written English.

4. Underline the parts of the translation you had the most trouble with. At the end of your paper, comment on your process by answering these:

   a. How did your translation process differ from the one we suggested?

   b. What difficulties did you have and how did you resolve them?

   c. What did you learn from each of your readers?

   d. What was the most important thing you learned from this exercise?

Your translation will be evaluated on:
- content: accuracy of content (30%)
- style/tone: choice of words, level of detail (30%)
- composition: readability, flow, and coherence (30%)
- comments: your reflections about the process (10%)

"Can You Spare a Quarter?" by John Maucere

Instructions   You are to learn the story well enough to retell it in class. Do the following:

1. First, understand the story. Ask around for help with any signs you may not be sure of.

2. Do not write out the story. If you need to write something down, write an outline of the story or make a list of events that take place in the story to help you remember.

3. Tell the story to someone who has not seen the story and ask the person for feedback to make sure your retelling is clear and easy to follow.

Now, you are ready for the task. You may also be videotaped.

ASSIGNMENT 8

"The Igorot People" by Cinnie MacDougall

Instructions
- Copy the outline onto a separate piece of paper leaving room to add answers.
- Develop a detailed outline of the video story. Use short sentences or phrases to complete the outline.

    I. **Introduction** (5 points)

   II. **Background** (40 points)
     A. Geography (list five facts about the Philippines)
       1.
       2.
       3.
       4.
       5.

  III. **The Igorots** (40 points)
     A. Location
     B. What the People Look Like
       1. Men (list 8 facts)
       2. Women (list 3 facts)
     C. Housing
     D. Occupations
       1. Women
       2. Men

  IV. **The Rice Terraces** (30 points)
     A. Facts (list 4 facts about the role of rice there and about the terraces)

   V. **Closing** (10 points)
     A. Opinions (list opinions Cinnie has about the rice terraces)

Malibu Vice   There is a bonus story at the end of the Signing Stories video. Watch and enjoy.